Identification

Troll

by Debra Clark

Published by Hobby House Press, Inc.
Cumberland, Maryland 21502

DEDICATION

I would like to thank some important people in my life for their support and encouragement in writing this book: my husband Jeff, for putting up with a troll takeover of our home for the past twelve years; my two daughters — Megan, age seven, for helping me out with her little sister, and Elizabeth, age three months, for being such a good sport at a very young age; my mom, for her "go for it" spirit and all her help and advice; my sister Donna, for babysitting services and support; my brothers, Scott and Phil, for their encouragement; my step-dad George, for his support; Shirley Bertrand, for telling Gary Ruddell about me and about my trolls; Gary Ruddell, for making a dream of mine come true; Lisa Kerner and Richard O'Krogly, for sending me their trolls by overnight express to be photographed the next day; my sister-in-law Kathie, whose beautiful photography is shown in this book; and to all my troll pals, for writing and sharing their collections with me and helping me to learn so much about trolls.

Additional copies of this book may be purchased at $9.95
from
HOBBY HOUSE PRESS
900 Frederick Street
Cumberland, Maryland 21502
or from your favorite bookstore or dealer.
Please add $3.25 per copy for postage.

TABLE OF CONTENTS

INTRODUCTION

This book is designed to help you identify and price your trolls. Whether you collect vinyl trolls or all different types of trolls, you will find a wide variety of collectible trolls in this book. Not every troll made is featured. It is impossible for one person to know every single item that was produced during the "troll craze" of the 1960s. I have tried to show you most of the rarer items I have come across over the years. I have been collecting trolls for twelve years, and to this day I am amazed at what I find. My book focuses primarily on unusual trolls because most collectors are familiar with the more common trolls. The common trolls are featured at the ends of Chapters VI and VII.

With all collectibles *condition* is the most important factor in establishing value, and trolls are no exception. I have tried to feature trolls in excellent or in better condition in this book. The most important feature of a troll is the hair. It can either be mohair (mostly seen in older models), fun fur, nylon, or synthetic. Please remember that if the hair has been cut, is missing, or is very sparse, this devalues a troll.

If the troll is made out of vinyl, as is most common, the condition of the vinyl is very important. If the vinyl has ink stains, magic marker, or dirt that just will not come off, your troll is worth much less money. I have tried to remove stains with cleanser, diluted bleach, acne medications, rubbing alcohol, nail polish remover, and by setting the troll out in the sun. Stains may fade a bit, but they never disappear completely. After 25 to 30 years, a stain is unfortunately more or less there to stay!

Clothing is another major feature. Look very carefully to see if the clothes are homemade. Most troll clothing has no labels sewn in. The only exceptions are the outfits of *some* of the 12in (31cm) trolls. Most troll clothing is made of felt. Commercially produced clothing does not have the jagged edges that scissors produce. The same goes for lettering in felt. These letters are die-cut, resulting in much cleaner edges than can be cut with scissors. On the clothing of 12in (31cm) trolls, you will find Velcro™ along the sides of pant seams and on shirts in some outfits such as the *Sailor's* costume. The reason for this is that trolls have wide legs and wide arms and are hard to dress. I have only seen Velcro™ used on 12in (31cm) outfits. It will look old also. Not all troll clothing is made of felt, but the outfit should still fit like a glove if the troll is in original clothes. After you have collected for a time, you will be able to tell whether clothing is original.

Please remember these factors when pricing and buying trolls. Missing or cracked eyes will also decrease the value of trolls.

Most important of all, remember that this book is a guide. Prices will vary depending on where you live and on rarity and demand. I am from the Midwest, so my price estimates may be lower than prices you find in your area. I must also note that as with any collectible, a troll is only worth what someone is willing to pay for it.

I hope you enjoy this book as much as I loved having the opportunity to write it. If you are not a collector of trolls, I think you will be fascinated by how diversified they truly are. If you are a collector of trolls, I hope this book increases your knowledge of them.

I am always interested in hearing from other troll collectors and in learning what they have in their collections. If you would like to write to me, my address is: P.O. Box 621, Algonquin, IL 60102.

Happy troll collecting!!!

Debra Clark

TROLL FOLKLORE

Trolls are simply defined as supernatural beings. According to Scandinavian folklore, trolls have been around for centuries. They are generally thought of as being very ugly, with long noses that have warts on them. Trolls have tails, and they have four fingers on each hand. They are very dirty and smell terribly. They can be ugly or pretty (rarely), fat or skinny, tall or short, good (rarely) or bad. Trolls dislike humans and cause them a great deal of trouble. Trolls are very selfish; they feel everything in the world belongs to them. They think, for example, that they own the trees, lakes, mountains, and caves. They will harm anyone who dares to come near them.

Not all trolls are mean. Some good trolls can be found. In Norwegian folklore, there is the *Jule-Nissen*, the Christmas troll, who comes down from the mountains for the twelve-day period of Christmas. He searches out a farm family to visit, and if he is treated kindly, he stays the full twelve days. The *Jule-Nissen* supposedly has the power to bring good luck to the family and good health to the animals. He loves animals. On Christmas Eve the Norwegian wife makes a pudding called *Romnegrot* for her family. If she is kind, she leaves a bowl in the barn for the *Jule-Nissen*. If the pudding is gone the next morning, the family wonders if he visited or if the barn cat ate the pudding. The moral of the story is that if you are kind and thoughtful to others, you will be a better person in the long run. Norwegian folktales always have a moral.

Some trolls are mean even to children. For example, there is a troll called *Tann-Verk-Trollet* (the toothache troll). He comes out at night and checks the teeth of a sleeping child. If the child did not brush his teeth, the troll quickly takes out a hammer and chisel and proceeds to make a hole in a tooth. This will become the troll's new home. The child awakens the next morning to a nasty toothache and never forgets to brush his teeth again! Another troll called *Har-Lugg-Trollet* makes his home in a child's hair and causes snarls. The child learns to keep his hair combed so this troll will not visit.

One troll story I enjoy is about *Huldra Troll*. She is a very ugly and mean troll, but she can put on a magical cap that makes her beautiful. She has a tail, which she tries to hide under her dress. When she flirts with a young man, her tail usually comes out, and a smart young man knows to run away from her. If a man notices only her face and not the rest of *Huldra Troll*, and if she can get him to marry her in a Christian church, her tail will fall off. However, she is still a mean troll, and she will make her husband's life miserable. He needs to be taught that he should marry a girl for her true self and not just because she has a pretty face.

It is a Scandinavian custom to have a troll in every home. If you treat your troll with love and kindness, he will bring good luck to your household. I hope this is true because I have many trolls living in my home! If you would like to learn more about troll folklore, the library is a good place to start. Books you may want to read include:

Scandinavian Folk & Fairy Tales, edited by Claire Booss, Avenel Books distributed by Crown Publisher, 1984.

Scandinavian Folktales, translated and edited by Jacqueline Simpson, Penguin Books, 1988.

Trolls, Trolls, Trolls, by Art "Grandpa" Stavig, Pine Hill Press, 1979.

A LITTLE BIT OF HISTORY

Trolls have existed for centuries according to Scandinavian folklore, but, for the troll collector, trolls have been around only since the early 1960s. Actually, in 1952 a Finnish couple, Helena and Martii Kuuskoski, made a pair of sawdust-filled cloth trolls with large ears, wide noses, and that wild hair for their children for Christmas. They eventually began producing trolls commercially and called them *Fauni Trolls*. Approximately 150,000 were sold in the 1950s. In the late 1950s, a Danish woodcarver named Thomas Dam carved his version of a troll for his daughter's birthday. She loved the troll and showed it to others in the village, where it was seen by a Danish toy merchant. A troll craze was born!

By the early 1960s, Thomas Dam had three factories producing his trolls in Denmark, in New Zealand and in Hialeah, Florida. Mrs. Inge Dykins of Denmark introduced the trolls to the U.S. market. An overwhelming demand for them began. As with anything popular, demand led to many manufacturers copying the design. This is the reason so many trolls are unmarked. The manufacture of unmarked trolls was a way of making a quick buck and avoiding copyright infringement lawsuits.

Dam Things Establishment sued Scandia House Enterprises in the '60s, claiming copyright infringement. The judge ruled that trolls were in the "public domain" and that, therefore, Scandia House did not violate any copyright laws. Eventually Dam

Things and Scandia House formed a partnership, and Scandia House gained the exclusive rights to manufacture and distribute the new line of Thomas Dam trolls in the U.S. market. Scandia House Enterprises was a division of Royalty Designs of Florida. Inge Dykins represented Scandia House Enterprises, and Thomas Dam owned Dam Things Establishment. Uneeda Doll and Toy Company also manufactured its own line of trolls called *Wishniks®*. A great number of trolls were produced and exported by Hong Kong and Japan; these were cheap imitations compared to the quality vinyl trolls made by the three major manufacturers mentioned above. Most of the 3in (8cm) trolls are unmarked, and it is difficult to know who made them.

In the 1990s, a new troll craze began and continues today. The Thomas Dam line of trolls is now manufactured exclusively by EFS Marketing Associates, based in New York, under the Norfin® trademark. Russ Berrie & Company, based in New Jersey, markets its own line of trolls, as does Ace Novelty Company, out of Washington, under the *Treasure Trolls™* trademark. Applause Toys makes its own line of trolls called *Magical Trolls™*. Uneeda Doll Company is still manufacturing its line of *Wishniks®* in the 1990s. There are also many unmarked trolls coming out of China and Korea. As I write this book, I cannot keep up with the troll craze of the '90s. Like all fads, the '90s troll craze eventually will fade, but for those of us who are collectors, the quest for trolls never does.

REFERENCES:
Newsweek, February 1963, "Life & Leisure" column.
Rarities, March/April 1983.
Scandinavian Folk & Fairy Tales, edited by Claire Booss, Avenel Books distributed by Crown Publisher, 1984.
Scandinavian Folktales, translated and edited by Jacqueline Simpson, Penguin Books, 1988.
Trolls, Trolls, Trolls, by Art "Grandpa" Stavig, Pine Hill Press, 1979.
Wall Street Journal, March 27, 1992, Marketplace section.

Caption descriptions run from left to right on photographs.

WHERE TO BUY AND SELL TROLLS

Where can you find trolls? At the present time it is no problem to find new trolls. Almost every store has some sort of troll merchandise available. You can find troll dolls, lunchboxes, notebooks, coloring books, bed linen sets, beach towels, and bath towels. I have seen lamps, banks, wind-up trolls, stickers, stationery, stuffed trolls, and boardgames, also shampoo, perfume, and Halloween costumes. These are only a few examples of what is now available.

Finding older trolls is a different story. Most of the trolls pictured in this book are from the 1960s. I have gone to countless flea markets, doll shows, antique shows, thrift stores, and garage sales. I have also found trolls at antique shops, but these trolls are usually over-priced.

I know of two troll clubs. I belong to both of them. One produces *Troll Monthly*, published by Lisa Kerner. Troll collectors from all over advertise their troll wants and their trolls for sale. Advertising is free with a year's subscription. *Troll Monthly* also includes articles on trolls, and members can submit a photo of their favorite troll for the monthly "Troll Profile."

The other troll club is the *Norfin®* *Fan Club*. They issue a newsletter twice a year. For those who are seeking penpals who love to collect trolls, the *Norfin® Club's* newsletter lists names and addresses of people who want penpals. There are also many different doll magazines and doll newspapers available.

When you do buy trolls through the mail, be careful and to ask questions. There are many new trolls now on the market. You must learn the difference between old and new trolls. Unfortunately this is a skill that is learned over many years of collecting. Please study your old trolls and learn their different markings and features. Most old trolls have mohair and are made of good quality vinyl. If you are looking for trolls made of different types of materials, you will find them in Scandinavian shops. The most important advice I can give you is to enjoy your troll collecting. Whether you have five or 5,000 trolls, if you no longer enjoy finding them or cannot afford them, it is time for you to move on.

Below are the addresses of the two troll clubs I mentioned. If you know of another troll club, please write to me at the address provided at the conclusion of the introduction.

Troll Monthly
c/o Trolling Along
585 Washington Street
Whitman, MA 02382

Norfin® Fan Club
c/o EFS Marketing Associates
164 Central Avenue
Farmingdale, NY 11735

CHAPTER I
Animals

When buying old trolls, the first question the collector usually asks is: "Do you have any animal trolls?" Animal trolls are the most popular and are considered the most desirable by troll collectors. Luckily for us, a wide variety of animal trolls can be found, as you will see in this chapter.

MONKEY TROLLS

THOMAS DAM: 7in (18cm). Wooly brown short mohair. Dark reddish brown eyes. Original clothes. Missing sailor cap. Marked: "Thomas Dam" on back. Original red plastic wrist tag. Tag marked: "Made in Denmark GJ0L." Has distinctive fingernails and toenails. Made of vinyl. Very hard to find. *Value:* mint with tag, $300; nude, $150.

THOMAS DAM: 2½in (6cm). Dark brown wooly mohair tucked under original red felt hat. Brown eyes. Original red plastic seal tag around waist. Body marked: "©Dam Things 1965, Design Dam Patent" on bottom of feet. All vinyl. Does not have distinctive toenails or fingernails. Very hard to find. *Value:* $65-$100.

R. SHEKTER: 6¼in (16cm). Black mohair. Brown eyes. Fingers are curled under. Has tail but no hair on tail. Textured, squeezable vinyl. Marked: "© R. Shekter 1966." *Value:* $45-$65.

R. SHEKTER: 3½in (9cm). Long white mohair. Orange-brown eyes. Textured, squeezable vinyl. Head not jointed. Marked: "© R. Shekter 1966." *Value:* $25-$35.

INTERNATIONAL MONKEY BUSINESS: 6¼in (16cm). White mohair on head and chest. Blue plastic eyes. Original green felt scarf. Original gold foil tag pasted to scarf, marked: "Leprechaun Good Luck Coin." Body marked: "Intern'l Monkey Bus. 19©67." Textured, squeezable vinyl. Also came with paper passport. He is called *Gorgeous Gorilla. Value:* $35-$55

TURTLES

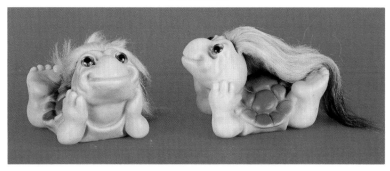

DAM THINGS EST.: (left) 3¼in (8cm). Long blonde mohair. Amber glass eyes. Hard vinyl. Green scaled shell. Marked: "Dam Things Est. 1964 Design Dam" on bottom. Very hard to find. *Value:* $150-$250.

DAM THINGS EST.: (right) 3¼in (8cm). Salt and pepper long mohair. Amber glass eyes. Marked: same as turtle on left. *Value:* $150-$250.
(Turtle on left is also shown on front cover.)

DONKEYS

DAM THINGS EST.: (left) 9in (23cm). Long white mohair on head and tail. Amber glass inset eyes. Hard, heavy textured vinyl. Jointed head. Marked: "© Dam Things Est. 1964" on bottom of foot. *Value:* $150-$175.

DAM THINGS EST.: 2¼in (6cm). White mohair. Amber glass inset eyes. Molded in sitting position. Hard vinyl. Marked: "Dam Things Establishment 1964" and "Design Dam" on bottom. *Value:* $20-$35.

JAPAN: 4in (10cm). Brownish-black rabbit fur hair on head and face. Amber plastic eyes. Red painted mouth. Original paper heart tag reads: "The Loveable Uglies With Removable Heads Japan." Body marked: "Made in Japan" on bottom of belly. Cheaper squeezable vinyl. *Value:* with tag, $20; without tag, $10-$15.

HONG KONG: 5¼in (13cm). Black rabbit fur hair. Orange plastic spiral eyes. Green cheap plastic body and head. Purple painted lips. Marked: "Made in Hong Kong" on bottom of belly. Hard to find in this size and color. *Value:* $20-$30.

ELEPHANTS

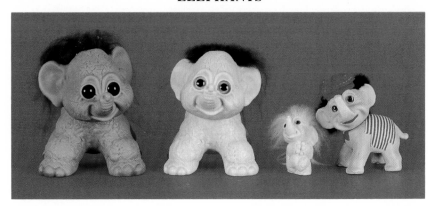

DAM THINGS EST.: 5½in (14cm). Dark brown eyes. Black mohair. Textured, scaled, squeezable, grayish-brown vinyl skin. Marked: "Made in Denmark, Dam Patent." Head jointed. Very hard to find in this color. *Value:* $175-$225.

DAM THINGS EST.: 5½in (14cm). Fleshtone hard vinyl. Marked: "© Dam Things Est. 1964" on bottom of foot. *Value:* $150-$200.

DAM THINGS EST.: 2¾in (7cm). Long peach mohair. Amber eyes. Hard, textured, scaly vinyl skin. Marked: "Dam Things Est. 1964" and "Dam Design Patent" on bottom. Elephant molded in sitting position. *Value:* $20-$35.

JAPAN: 3¾in (10cm). Black pasted on rabbit fur hair. Brown plastic eyes. Red painted mouth. Blue squeezable cheaper vinyl. Original red flannel cap, bow tie, red and white striped saddle. Marked: "Made in Japan" on bottom of belly. No hair on tail. I believe the Japan/Hong Kong elephants, donkeys, giraffes, and tigers did not come with hair on their tails. I have never found any with hair. *Value:* with clothes, $20; nude, $10-$15.

LIONS

THOMAS DAM: 5in (13cm). Amber glass eyes. Black mohair. Black painted nose. Heavy vinyl. Marked: "Design Dam Patent." More easily found than other large Dam animals. *Value:* $65-$115.

JAPAN: 4in (10cm). Black rabbit fur hair on head and tail. Black painted nose and red painted mouth. Amber plastic eyes. Marked: "Made in Japan" on bottom of belly. Cheaper vinyl. *Value:* $10-$20.

HONG KONG: 3¼in (8cm). Black rabbit fur on head only. Amber plastic eyes. Pink cheaper plastic body and head. Marked: "Made in Hong Kong" on bottom of belly. *Value:* $5-$15.

THOMAS DAM: 11½in (29cm). Long salt and pepper mohair. Amber glass eyes. Light pink painted lips. Marked: "Thomas Dam, Made in Denmark." Heavy vinyl. *Value:* $85-$125.

JAPAN: 5in (13cm). Black rabbit fur on head and around neck. Amber plastic eyes. Black painted nose. Red painted mouth. Brown spots on body. Marked: "Made in Japan." Original paper tag around neck. *Value:* $10-$20.

HONG KONG: 3¼in (10cm). Blue fun fur on head, possibly original. Amber plastic eyes. All blue body and head. Slight red painted lips. Cheap plastic. *Value:* $5-$10.

UNMARKED THOMAS DAM: 6in (15cm). Long magenta colored mohair. Amber glass eyes. Cow bell has been replaced. Unmarked. (I have one that is marked "Dam Design Patent.") *Value:* $125-$200.

DAM THINGS EST.: 2¼in (6cm). Long white mohair. Brown glass eyes. Cows have molded tails and udder, and horns on top of head. Hard vinyl. Marked: "© Dam Things Est. 1964" and "Design Dam" on bottom of feet. Most Dam animals come in four different hair colors: peach, white, black, and brown, and in a salt and pepper combo.

Occasionally you will find them with green, red, purple, or pink hair; these colors are harder to find. *Value:* $20-$35.

DAM THINGS EST.: 2½in (6cm). Long lavender mohair. Green spiral eyes. The small horse has long mohair for the tail. This one has a felt green and yellow saddle. Not all horses come with a saddle. Marked: "© Dam Things Est. 1964" on bottom of foot; "Design Dam" on bottom of belly. *Value:* $20-$35; unusual hair color with saddle, $35-$45.

THOMAS DAM MOUSE: 5in (13cm).
Brown short fun fur hair. Dark brown glass
eyes. All gray-brown body and head. Head
not jointed. Soft vinyl. Original clothes. Black
painted nose with nylon whiskers rooted on
sides of nose. Marked: "T.H. Dam Design ©
1967" on bottom of foot. Has a long molded
tail with no hair on it. I believe he was made
in the early 1970s. Very hard to find. *Value:*
$50-$75.

MISCELLANEOUS TROLL ANIMALS

BEAR: 7in (18cm). Unmarked. White mohair on head. Blue plastic eyes. Thinner vinyl with molded hair on arms, chest, back, feet, ears, and back of head. Black painted nose. Hard to find. *Value:* $35-$75.

FOX: 6½in (17cm). White mohair on head and chest. Aqua colored eyes. White painted tail. Thinner rubbery vinyl with molded hair on body and face. Black painted nose. Original red felt coat. Original gold foil tag. Tag marked: "© Leprechaun LTD. 1970." Passport name: *Wiley Fox.* Body is unmarked. *Value:* $35-$65.

JAPAN TIGER: 4½in (12cm). Black rabbit fur on head. Amber plastic eyes. Black painted nose and whiskers. Red painted mouth. Light brown felt cap on head. Blue and white striped saddle.

Red tie pasted on chest. All yellow cheaper vinyl with stripes. Marked: "17 Made in Japan." Hard to find. *Value:* $15- $30.

ROYALTY DESIGNS DOG: 3in (8cm). Long black mohair. White and black plastic eyes. Black painted nose. Original astronaut outfit. Hard vinyl with molded tail. Marked: "© Roy. Des. of Fla. 1967." Hard to find. *Value:* dressed in original clothes, $40; nude, $15-$30.

ROYALTY DESIGNS CAT: 3in (8cm). Red mohair. Black and white plastic eyes. Molded tail. Hard vinyl. Marked: "© Roy. Des. of Fla. 1967." Hard to find. *Value:* nude, $15-$30; dressed, $40.

DISCONTINUED NORFIN® ANIMAL BANKS

SQUIRREL: 6½in (17cm). Brown/orange eyes. Vinyl. Original plastic bag reads "Original Lykketroll FRA GJOL Dam" (not pictured). Comes with metal key. Hard to find. Year made is unknown. Marked: "Thomas Dam." *Value:* $75.

BEAR: 6½in (17cm). Brown eyes. Marked: "T Dam Orig." Norfin® Tag. Comes with plastic key. *Value:* $50.

MOUSE: 6½in (17cm). Brown eyes. Original blue felt scarf around neck. Marked: "Made in Denmark 1984 © Dam" on bottom. Original Norfin® tag. *Value:* $50.

WHALE: 5in (13cm) at tip of tail. Blue eyes. Body marked: "Made in Denmark by Dam © 1984." Original Norfin® tag. Plastic key. *Value:* $40.

OLDER NORFIN® PIG: 6½in (17cm). Brown eyes. Fleshtone vinyl. Orange paint on nose, mouth, and hands not original. Clothes original. Blonde mohair pasted on head not original. Marked: "Thomas Dam." No key. I believe she was made in the 1970s or early 1980s. Note how her arms seem to be apart when compared to those of the other Norfin® pig shown beside her. Hard to find. *Value:* $75. *Courtesy of Lisa Kerner Collection.*

SEAL: 6½in (17cm). Brown eyes. Marked: "Dam © 1984 Made in Denmark by Dam." Original Norfin® tag. Comes with a plastic key. *Value:* $40.

PIG: 5¼in (15cm). Closed eyes. Fleshtone vinyl. Marked: "Dam." Original Norfin® tag. Named *Wilbur* on tag. *Value:* $35.

PIG: 6½in (17cm). Brown eyes. Fleshtone vinyl. Unmarked. Original blue felt scarf. Original Norfin® tag. Metal key. *Value:* $40.

TURTLE: 4in (10cm). Brown eyes. Green scaled back. Marked: "© Dam 1984." Original Norfin® tag. Plastic key. *Value:* $40.

LIMITED EDITION DAM ANIMALS

HORSE: 7in (18cm). Brown eyes. Orange mohair on head and all mohair tail. Body is unmarked. The Limited Edition animals are reissued from molds made in the 1960s. They are marketed by EFS Marketing Associates, Inc. They made 500 each of the horse, elephant, cow, and lion. Each has a gold cardboard label around its leg. Label reads: "Limited Edition Made in Denmark The Troll Company ApS © 1990 Thomas Dam, Distributed By EFS Marketing Assoc. Inc." Issue price for Norfin® Club Members was $50 each. The horses are the only ones that have mohair. The other three animals have synthetic hair. They also have a darker fleshtone vinyl than the older animals. EFS Marketing Associates, Inc. has sold out of these animals. *Value:* $65 each.

HORSE: Pink mohair on head and tail. Gray colored vinyl. Brown eyes. Unmarked. *Value:* $65.

ELEPHANT: 6in (15cm). Brown eyes. Pink short synthetic hair. Pink felt scarf. Gray colored vinyl, scaly, wrinkled skin. Marked: "Made in Denmark Dam Patent" on bottom of foot. Note white airbrushed ears. *Value:* $65.

COW: 6½in (17cm). Brown eyes. Light tan colored synthetic hair. Green felt scarf. Body marked: "Made in Denmark Thomas Dam." Fleshtone vinyl. *Value:* $65.

LION: 5½in (14cm). Brown eyes. Auburn colored synthetic hair on head and tail. Body marked: "Dam Patent, Made in Denmark GJ0L" on bottom of feet. *Courtesy of Lisa Kerner Collection.*

18

PORCU-PEN: 3¼in (8cm). Brown eyes. Brown-colored back has holes in it to hold pens and pencils. Marked: "© Dam Nitusch R Made in Denmark 1986." Original Norfin® tag. Does not have a bank slot. *Value:* $35.

PORCUPINE PEN HOLDER: 1½in (4cm) tall and 4½in (12cm) long. Brown eyes. Comes with two pencils and two trolls made of hard plastic. Label on bag reads "Made in China." He is called *Tommy Troll*. *Value:* mint in box, $15.

The animals shown in this chapter are ones I have in my collection (except where other credits are noted). Thomas Dam also made an alligator troll of which I have seen a photocopied picture. The alligator comes in two different sizes. One appears to be 3in (8cm) tall and the other around 6in (15cm) tall with mohair on the tops of their heads. They appear to have a hard, scaly, vinyl skin. They are very rare. *Value:* 3in (8cm), $150-$300; 6in (15cm), $350+.

I also have the so-called goat troll. He is like the large Dam donkey only he has a mohair beard pasted under his chin. I have not seen another goat troll, so I cannot confirm mine is an actual goat. I am sure there are other animals to be found. As you can see, there is quite a variety to look for. EFS Marketing Associates, Inc., does sell small Dam animals in their Norfin® line. They are called *Norfin's Ark*™.

19

CHAPTER II
Large Trolls

Some of the largest trolls made in the 1960s range from 11in (28cm) to 18in (46cm). They include vinyl trolls and stuffed body trolls with vinyl arms and heads. The 11in (28cm) and 12in (31cm) Dam Things Est. trolls came in a variety of costumes. One of the most sought after is the 12in (31cm) black troll and the *Santa Claus* troll made by Dam Things Est.

BLACK TROLL: 12in (31cm). Amber glass eyes. Black short mohair. Marked: "Dam Things Est. 1964" on back of neck. Redressed. She has painted pink lips but most of the paint is worn. *Value:* redressed, $200; dressed in original clothes, $300+. *(Also shown on front cover.)*

SANTA CLAUS: 12in (31cm). White mohair hair and beard. Green glass eyes. Original clothes. Marked: "Dam Things Est. 1964" on back of neck and bottom of foot. *Value:* $150-$225.

PLAYBOY: 12in (31cm). Fire engine red mohair. Blue inset eyes. Original clothes. Marked: "Dam Things Est. 1964" on back of neck and bottom of foot. I have seen these with pink, orange, and aqua blue mohair. *Value:* $125-$175.

WOODY HAYES: 12in (31cm). Yellow mohair. Green glass eyes. Original clothes. Original felt pennant that fits inside a small hole in his hand. Made for the Rose Bowl. Marked: "Dam Things Est. 1964" on back of neck and bottom of foot. *Value:* $150-$200.

WAC: 12in (31cm). Long yellow mohair. Brown glass eyes. Original clothes. Marked: "Dam Things Est. 1964" on back of neck and bottom of foot. *Value:* $125-$175.
ARMY: 12in (31cm). Long black mohair. Amber glass eyes. Original clothes. His clothes have a sewn in tag which reads, "© 1964 65 Dam Things Est. Mfg. by Royalty Design of Florida Inc., Hialeah, Florida." Body marked: "Dam Things Est. 1964" on bottom of foot and back of foot and back of neck. *Value:* $125-$175.

CLOWN: 12in (31cm). Pink short mohair. Blue glass eyes. Original clothes. Clothes are tagged on the side. Not all 12in (31cm) trolls' clothing is tagged. Body marked: "Dam Things Est. 1964" on back of neck and bottom of foot. I have seen this outfit with a striped print. *Value:* $100-$165.

SAILOR: 12in (31cm). Long blonde mohair. Amber glass eyes. Original clothes. Original paper tag around neck reads, "Iggy Normus™ Dam Things Originals © 1964-1965 Dam Things Est. MFG. by Royalty Designs of Fla., Inc." Inside tells how the Dam Troll originated. Body marked: "Dam Things Est. 1964" on back of neck and bottom of foot. *Value:* $125-$175.

ETHNIC BOY: 12in (31cm). Short blue mohair. Blue glass eyes. Original clothes. Marked: "© Dam Things Est. 1964" on back of neck and bottom of foot. *Value:* $125-$175.

CAVEMAN: 12in (31cm). Short peach mohair. Brown glass eyes. Original outfit. Most commonly found outfit on the 12in (31cm) size. Original paper tag. Marked: "©Dam Things Est. 1964" on back of neck and bottom of foot. *Value:* $100-$135.

HOBO: 12in (31cm). Long white mohair; bottom half of mohair is black. Brown glass eyes. Original clothes. Marked: "© Dam Things Est. 1964" on bottom of foot and back of neck. Clothes are tagged. *Value:* $100-$150.

HOBO: 12in (31cm). White mohair. Brown glass eyes. Original clothes. Notice the slightly different print. Body marked: "© Dam Things Est. 1964" on back of neck and bottom of foot. *Value:* $100-$150.

GRANDPA: 11in (28cm). White mohair and beard. Green eyes. Redressed. Marked: "©Dam Things Est. 1964" on back of neck and bottom of foot. *Value:* redressed, $100; original clothes, $125-$175.

TARTAN GIRL: 12in (31cm). Short white mohair. Brown glass eyes. Original clothes. Marked: "© Dam Things Est. 1964." *Value:* $100-$150.

YE YE: 12in (31cm). Long orange mohair. Green glass eyes. Original felt clothes. Marked: "©Dam Things Est. 1964" on back of neck and bottom of foot. *Value:* $125-$165.

GIRL IN PINK JUMPER: 12in (31cm). Long pink mohair. Dark blue glass eyes. Commonly found outfit. Boys will have shorts with straps. Marked: "© Dam Things Est.1964" on back of neck and bottom of foot. *Value:* $85-$115.

NEWER DAM BOY: 11in (28cm). Yellow synthetic hair. Amber eyes. Original felt clothes. This style of troll is a lighter vinyl with a lighter skin tone than the older versions. I believe these were made in the early 1970s. Marked: "© Dam Things Est. 1964" on back of neck and bottom of foot. *Value:* $65-$95.

NEWER DAM GIRL: 11in (28cm). Pink synthetic short hair. Orange plastic eyes. Original clothes. Marked: "© Dam Things Est. 1964" on back of neck and bottom of foot. *Value:* $65-$95.

UNMARKED GIRL: 14in (36cm). Magenta mohair with black tips. Orange bulging plastic eyes. Pink painted lips. Nude. I believe these were made by Scandia House Enterprises. *Value:* dressed in original clothes, $100-$135; nude, $65-$100.

UNMARKED CAVEMAN: 14in (36cm). Long peach colored mohair. Orange bulging plastic eyes. Original clothes. Pink painted lips. Most commonly found outfit in this size troll. *Value:* $75-$125.

UNMARKED STUFFED BODY TROLL:
18½in (47cm). Short blue synthetic hair.
Orange bulging eyes. Pink lips. Stuffed blue
body with soft vinyl head. This may be *Happy*
Homer, "The Giant Troll Good Luck Mascot." He came with a ball-point pen for
autographing. Redressed. Very hard to find.
Value: $125-$175.

SCANDIA HOUSE STUFFED BOY: 11in (28cm). Long white mohair. Brown plastic eyes. Original clothes are sewn into the body. They are not meant to come off. Marked: "Scandia House Enterprises" on the back of his neck. Original heart sticker is on his chest. Sticker reads, "© Scandia House Enterprises Inc. 1965 True Troll." *Value:* $55-$95.

SCANDIA HOUSE STUFFED GIRL: 11in (28cm). Yellow mohair with black tips. Green plastic eyes. Original outfit. Both girls are stuffed bodies with vinyl arms and heads. Marked: "Scandia House Enterprises" on back of neck. *Value:* $55-$95.

SCANDIA HOUSE GIRL IN PRINT DRESS: 11½in (29cm). Long white mohair. Blue plastic eyes. Original blue print dress. Marked: "Scandia House Enterprises" on back of neck. *Value:* $55-$95.

There is also a graduate version. The clothes are tagged "IDEAL." This is a much harder version to find. VALUE: $75-$125.

STUFFED TEDDY BEAR TROLL: 19in (48cm). Yellow synthetic hair. Brown painted molded eyes with black painted pupils. Red painted tongue. Stuffed pink body. Original blue felt vest with jute ties. Marked: "TIME" under chin. *Value:* $65-$100.

STUFFED TEDDY BEAR TROLL: 19in (48cm). Orange synthetic hair. Brown painted molded eyes with black painted eyes. Lime green stuffed body with vinyl face. Original yellow felt vest with jute ties. Marked: "TIME" under chin. *Value:* $65-$100.

CHAPTER III
Santas, Vikings, and Mint in Box Trolls

This chapter features some of the most sought after trolls. Collectors are always particularly happy to acquire a *Santa* troll, a Viking troll, or anything mint in box. As you will see, quite a variety exists in all three areas.

SANTAS

DAM THINGS EST.: 7½in (19cm). Long white mohair and beard. This particular troll also has a moustache. He is not a bank. Amber glass eyes. Complete *Santa* suit. Marked: "Thomas Dam Danmark" on back and "USA Foreign Pats Pending, Denmark" on back of neck. Original troll sticker on bottom of foot. Hard to find with moustache. *Value:* $80-$100.

DAM THINGS EST. BANK: 7in (18cm). Long white mohair and beard. Green inset eyes. Complete *Santa* suit. Marked: "Thomas Dam" on back. He is a bank and has a vertical slot on his back. Most easily found of the *Santa* trolls. *Value:* $45-$65.

UNMARKED *SANTA:* 7in (18cm). Long white synthetic hair and beard. Complete *Santa* suit. Note that he has black nylon tights; these are his boots. Orange spiral inset eyes. Hard to find. *Value:* $45-$75.

UNUSUAL *SANTA* BANK: 7½in (19cm). White fun fur hair. Amber plastic eyes. Complete *Santa* suit. Marked: "© Huron Products Co." on bottom of foot and "Creative Mfg., Inc. 1978" on back of neck. Hard to find. *Value:* $45-$65.

THOMAS DAM: 5½in (14cm). White mohair and beard. Blue glass eyes. Original *Santa* suit, with cap missing. Marked: "Thomas Dam" on back. This size is hard to find.

The 7in (18cm) bank and 3in (8cm) *Santas* are much easier to find. *Value:* $25-$45.

SCANDIA HOUSE ENT.: 5½in (14cm). White mohair and beard. Green spiral eyes. Complete *Santa* suit with black tights as "boots." Marked: "K-2" on back of head. Hard to find. This troll is not marked as being by Scandia House Enterprises, but I have found this same style of troll with its original red heart sticker and tag indicating it is a Scandia House troll. *Value:* $25-$45.

CHUNK-O-LUCK: 2¾in (7cm). Long white mohair and painted, molded beard. Green spiral eyes. Hard rubber body. He has five fingers on each hand; most trolls have four fingers on each hand and four toes on each foot. His ears also resemble half of a four-leaf clover. Marked: "CHUNK-O-LUCK CO." on his back. His clothes are painted on. Hard to find. *Value:* $25-$35. *Richard O'Krogly Collection.*

SANTA **ORNAMENT:** 1½in (4cm) tall. Pencil topper troll. Troll glued on red flocked ball ornament. Long white mohair. Green plastic eyes. Complete *Santa* suit. Hangs on the tree by a gold cord. Troll marked: "S.H.E.

UNEEDA WISHNIK®: 5½in (14cm). Long white mohair. Amber plastic eyes. Complete *Santa* suit. Marked: "Uneeda *Wishnik*™ Patent No. #D190-918" on back. Hard to find. *Value:* $25-$45.

JAPAN: 5in (13cm). White mohair. Brown plastic eyes. Cheaper thin plastic body and head. Complete *Santa* suit. Marked: "Made in Japan" on back. Hard to find. *Value:* $20-$35.

1964" on back. Very rare. *Value:* $25-$35.

UNMARKED *SANTA* **VIKING:** 2½in (6cm). White mohair beard. Brown inset eyes. Red felt cap with mohair trim. Red painted body. Thinner vinyl body and head. Unmarked. Hard to find. *Value:* $25.

SANTA **PIN:** 1½in (4cm). Pencil topper troll. He also has a pin on his back. Long white mohair. Purple plastic eyes. Complete *Santa* suit. Marked: "S.H.E. 1964" on back. *Value:* $15-$25.

SCANDIA HOUSE ENT.: 2¾in (10cm). White mohair and beard. Green spiral eyes. Complete *Santa* suit. Unmarked. Original goldtone metal sleigh. The sleigh came with the troll and was sold in a candy store in California. It held peppermint candies *Value:* with sleigh, $35; troll only, $20.

UNMARKED: 2in (5cm). Long white mohair. No beard. Green eyes. Complete *Santa* suit. *Value:* $10-$20.

BLACK UNMARKED: 2½in (6cm). Orange mohair; his hair has been replaced but looks as it originally did. Orange spiral eyes. Pink painted lips. Complete *Santa* suit made of felt. Rare. *Value:* $25-$40.

DAM: 2½in (6cm). Long white mohair. Brown eyes. Complete *Santa* suit made of felt. Marked: "DAM" on back. *Value:* $10-$20.

UNMARKED TABNECK: 3in (8cm). White mohair tucked under cap. White fun fur beard. Gold inset eyes. Complete *Santa* suit made of flannel. He also has black shoes. Unmarked except for tab on back of neck. *Value:* $10-$15.

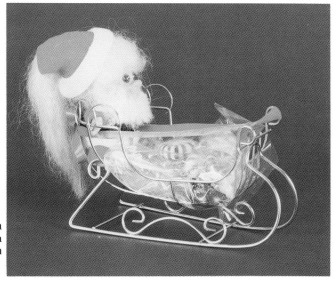

Closeup of Scandia House Ent. Santa and sleigh shown above.

29

DAM THINGS EST.: 6½in (17cm). Short wooly mohair and beard. Orange-brown glass eyes. Molded vinyl brown Viking hat. Original felt one-piece Viking suit with red leather belt. Marked: "Dam Things Est. 1965" on bottom of foot. Original red plastic wrist tag. Hard to find. *Value:* mint with tag, $150; dressed with tag, $125; dressed no tag, $85-$115; nude, $50-$75.

UNMARKED: 7in (18cm). Salt and pepper rabbit fur hair beard and rabbit fur on back of head. Molded, painted Viking hat. Blue glass eyes. Original felt one-piece suit. Blue felt cape. Black vinyl belt. Molded painted shoes. Unmarked. *Value:* dressed with cape, $65; nude, $35-$45.

UNMARKED: 6¼in (17cm). Ecru-colored mohair beard and around hat. Brown glass eyes. Molded, painted vinyl Viking hat. Red painted mouth. Original blue felt cape, suede one-piece outfit with leather belt. Painted molded boots. *Value:* dressed, $55; nude, $30.

UNMARKED: 4in (10cm). Gray wooly mohair on head and beard. Painted molded Viking hat. Blue plastic eyes. Original orange felt cape. Clothes are painted on. Fingers are curled under. Unmarked. *Value:* $30.

UNMARKED: 3¼in (9cm). Blue mohair beard. Brown glass eyes. Red painted mouth. Blue rubber Viking hat with rubber band hang cord. Body is vinyl. *Value:* $15-$25.

UNMARKED: 3in (8cm). Brown mohair beard. Brown glass eyes. Rubber molded Viking hat. Painted on clothes. Unmarked. *Value:* $15-$25.

REISLER KEYCHAIN: 2in (5cm). White pipe cleaner beard. Amber plastic eyes. Yellow felt cape; molded, painted clothes and hat. Marked: "Reisler Made in Denmark" on bottom of feet. You may find these at Scandinavian shops. They are not old. *Value:* $5.

MINT IN BOX TROLLS

THOMAS DAM PLAYBOY: 5½in (14cm). Yellow mohair wrapped around felt bunny ears. Blue glass eyes. Complete felt playboy bunny suit. Original clear thin plastic oval container. Troll marked: "Thomas Dam" on back; "Made in Denmark Foreign Pats Pending" on back of neck. *Value:* $60.

31

THOMAS DAM BRIDE: 5½in (14cm). Blue mohair. Brown glass eyes. Original bride outfit. Veil in hair. Marked: "Thomas Dam" on back; "Made in Denmark, Foreign Pats Pending" on back of neck. Original plastic container. *Value:* $60.

THOMAS DAM GIRL WITH MATCHING GIRL: 5½in (14cm). Orange mohair. Green glass eyes. Original felt clothes. Green felt tie in hair. Marked: "Thomas Dam" on back. 3in (8cm) matching girl is unmarked. *Note:* The package has four staple marks on the bottom of the container that match up perfectly to the trolls' feet. I believe these trolls were packaged together. Original plastic container. *Value:* mint in box, $75 pair.

32

UNEEDA *WISHNIK*® BASEBALL:
5½in (14cm). Long peach colored
mohair. Green plastic eyes. Original
baseball uniform. Troll marked:
"Uneeda Wishnik Patent No.#D190-
918" on back. Original thin plastic cyl-
inder container. *Value:* $55.

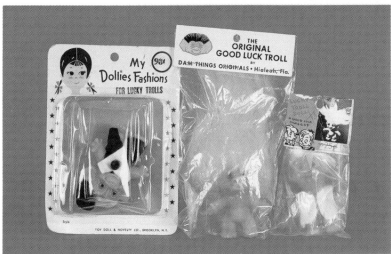

UNMARKED DOLLIES FASHIONS:
2¾in (7cm). Yellow "puff" ball hair. Orange
spiral eyes. Original tuxedo outfit. Troll unmarked. Package marked: "My Dollies Fashions For Lucky Troll Dolls. Toy Doll & Novelty
Co. Brooklyn, N.Y." *Value:* $25.
DAM THINGS EST.: 2¾in (7cm). Long yellow mohair. Brown glass eyes. Troll marked: "©

64" on back. Original poly bag with cardboard
header. *Value:* $20.
LUCKY TROLL DOLL VAMPIRE: 3in
(8cm). White rabbit fur hair. Gold plastic eye;
one eye is missing. Orange cheap plastic body
and head. Original vest. Marked: "Hong Kong"
on back. Original poly bag with cardboard header.
Note: the troll pictured on the header is not the
one in the bag. *Value:* $10-$15.

DAM THINGS *LUCKY STRIKE:* 2¾in (7cm). Long white mohair. Brown glass eyes, black painted "black eye" over right eye. Original clothes. Hat reads "I'd rather fight." I believe he was used to advertise *Lucky Strike*™ cigarettes. He is in his original hard plastic box. Note the Dam Things Est. head sticker on the front of the box. This troll is hard to find, as is this type of container. *Value:* $35.

DAM THINGS EST. ARMY: 2¾in (7cm). Long peach colored mohair. Brown glass eyes. Original green army suit. Original paper passport. Original container. *Value:* dressed with passport, $30.

SCANDIA HOUSE ENT.: 2½in (6cm). Long black mohair under straw hat. Green spiral eyes. Darker skin tone but not brown. Complete Hawaiian outfit with banjo. Troll unmarked. Original thin plastic oval container. *Value:* $25.

SCANDIA HOUSE ENT.: 2½in (6cm). Long blue mohair. Amber spiral eyes. Original white felt doctor's outfit. Comes with black plastic stethoscope. Troll unmarked. Original container. *Value:* $25.

SCANDIA HOUSE ENT.: 2½in (6cm). Long yellow mohair tied in a ponytail. Purple spiral eyes. Original cheerleader outfit with the words "Go Go" on skirt. She comes with white rubbery shoes stapled to feet. Troll unmarked. Original plastic container. *Value:* $25.

SCANDIA HOUSE ENT.: 2½in (6cm). Green mohair tucked under felt baseball cap. Green spiral eyes. Complete felt baseball uniform with brown plastic mitt and ball attached to hand. Original red heart sticker on container, indicating a Scandia House Enterprises 1965 troll. *Value:* $25.

DOUBLEHEADED TROLLS

UNEEDA *WISHNIK®:* 3in (8cm). One head has blue mohair and the other has white. Both have rose colored plastic eyes. Nude. Original container missing lid. Troll marked with double horseshoes on bottoms of feet. Some of the Uneeda *Wishnik* doubleheaded trolls do not have horseshoe marks; some have tabs on the bottoms of their feet. I do not know why they were marked differently. Very hard to find in original container. Please note the container will say "Double-Nik" and "Rub my hair for double luck" on it. *Value:* $65.

LUCKY *SHNOOKS:* 3in (8cm). Pink synthetic hair on one side and white on the other side. Right head has blue plastic eyes and left head has gold colored eyes. Nude. Body marked: "Hong Kong." Original poly bag with colorful cardboard header which features a picture of a vampire troll. Hard to find. *Value:* $40.

UNEEDA *WISHNIK®:* 3in (8cm). One side has yellow mohair and the other has green. Right head has rose colored eyes; the other has gold. Dressed in original denim overalls. Marked with double horseshoes on bottoms of feet. *Value:* no container, $45.

WISHNIKS® MINT IN BOX

UNEEDA *WISHNIK®* SQUARE CONTAINER: 2¾in (7cm). Red synthetic hair. This type of hair comes out easily; combing is not recommended. Gold colored eyes. Dressed in original robe. Has curlers for hair. I believe these were packaged nude trolls. A harder plastic container with hard plastic lid and bottom. I believe these containers are late 1960s or early 1970s. *Value:* $15.

UNEEDA *WISHNIK®:* 2¾in (7cm). Green synthetic hair. Amber plastic eyes. Nude. This hard plastic container has an oval shape. Troll has double horseshoes on bottoms of feet. This style is also a harder vinyl. *Value:* $15.

UNEEDA *WISHNIK®:* 2¾in (7cm). Brown synthetic hair. Amber eyes. Original oval container. *Value:* $15.

UNEEDA *WISHNIK®:* 2¾in (7cm). Red synthetic hair. Amber eyes. Original container. *Value:* $15.

35

UNEEDA *WISHNIK®*: 2¾in (7cm). White mohair. Blue plastic eyes. Original white angora bunny outfit. Troll is unmarked. Original oval thinner plastic container with lid missing. Container has blue printing on it. The other container shown has red printing. These were early 1960s containers. *Value:* $20.

UNEEDA *WISHNIK®*: 3in (8cm). Salt and pepper synthetic hair. Amber eyes. Dressed as Indian troll. I bought this one in this container but it is not an original container because this is a later version Uneeda *Wishnik* troll. *Value:* troll in original container, $20.

WISHNIKS® MINT IN PACKAGE

1981 REISSUED: 5½in (14cm). Blonde, very sparse synthetic hair. Comes out easily. Amber eyes. Complete cowboy outfit. These reissued trolls came out in 1981. They came in six different styles. These are clearly marked on the back "1966 Hong Kong." The older Uneeda *Wishniks®* are not dated. Please be careful when buying this size. Uneeda did make a late 1960s or early 1970s version with synthetic hair, but it was better quality. The vinyl is also heavier and darker skin tone. Older *Wishniks* are marked: "UNEEDA WISHNIK PATENT NO#D190-918" on their backs. *Value:* mint in package, $20; loose but dressed, $15; nude, $8.

1976 *WISHNIK®* MINT IN PACKAGE: 3in (8cm). Brown synthetic hair. Amber eyes. These came out in 1976. Hard vinyl construction. *Value:* $10.

BENDABLE *WISHNIK®*: 4½in (12cm). Blue synthetic hair. Amber plastic eyes. This is the *Cook-nik.* They were issued in 1982 and came in six different styles. Their body construction is a rubbery vinyl with wires inside so the trolls will bend into any pose. *Value:* mint in package, $15; loose but dressed in original clothes, $10; nude, $4.

BENDABLE *WISHNIK®*: 4½in (12cm). *Golf-nik* version. Please note that a 3in (8cm) Uneeda *Wishnik* was also reissued in original plastic containers. These came out in twelve different styles. The containers have an outer space motif. Please see Chapter IX for a picture of these. *Value:* mint in box, $10. This version came out in 1983. Occasionally you will find these in different color bodies. *Value:* mint in package, $15; loose, $10.

36

CHAPTER IV
Unusual Trolls in Vinyl

UNUSUAL COUPLES

THOMAS DAM: Girl is 8in (20cm) tall. Has orangish-gold colored mohair. Brown glass eyes. The mohair is actually stitched on to the vinyl. Their bodies are filled with a sawdust-like type of material. They are one-piece vinyl construction and are somewhat heavy. Clothes are felt and original. Girls come in the jumper style. Girls also have rounded ears. Her tag reads, "Garantimaerke Monsterbeskyttet og. Indreg. 11069BP Lykketrold Fra. GJ0L T.H. Dam Telepfon GJ0L 75 Gj0l PR AA bybro." Body is marked: "Dam Lykketroll Made in Denmark" on bottom of foot. Boy is 8½in (22cm) tall with black mohair that is also stitched on to his head. His clothes are original. He is missing his European market tag. I believe these were some of

the first trolls manufactured by Thomas Dam. They are the only ones by him I have found with sawdust-filled bodies and hair stitched on. Hard to find. *Value:* pair, $150; each, $75; nude, $50. *Richard O'Krogly Collection. (See back cover for color photograph.)*

UNMARKED: Boy is 7¾in (20cm) tall. He has pointed ears. Gold spiral plastic eyes. All one-piece molded vinyl body. Clothes are molded and painted. Note the very human shape to their bodies. They have five fingers on each hand. Girl is 7in (18cm) tall with white mohair. They are unmarked. A very rare pair. *Value:* pair, $125; each, $60. *(See title page for color photograph.)*

ROYALTY DESIGNS OF FLORIDA: Girl is 6¼in (16cm) tall. She has red mohair. Blue spiral plastic eyes. Original felt dress. Boy is 6¼in (16cm) tall and has green mohair and lavender spiral eyes. They are marked: "RDF 68" on back of neck and bottoms of feet. His clothes are original. Hard to find. *Value:* pair, $80; nude, $25 each.

TAILED TROLLS

DAM THINGS EST.: 6½in (17cm). Long gray mohair on head and tail. Amber glass eyes. Original burlap outfit. Comes with passport. Very hard vinyl. Head is jointed. Marked: "© Dam Things Est. 1965" on bottom of feet. He has very distinctive fingernails and toenails. Only the

tailed trolls and the 7in (18cm) Dam *Monkey* have this feature, with the exception of the 3in (8cm) version tailed troll. All of the Dam tailed trolls are greatly desired by collectors. *Value:* with clothes, original tag, and passport, $175; nude,: $95-$115.

DAM THINGS EST.: 3in (8cm). White mohair on head and tail. Brown glass eyes. Very hard vinyl. Head is jointed. Nude, originally dressed in burlap outfit. Marked: "©Dam Things EST. 1965" on bottom of feet. This is the hardest

of the tailed trolls to find. *Value:* dressed, $85; nude, $60.

DAM THINGS EST.: 2½in (6cm). Long pink mohair on head and tail. Blue glass eyes. Head is not jointed. Hard vinyl. Has distinctive fingernails and toenails. Marked: "©Dam Things Est. 1965" on bottom of foot. I have never found one dressed. *Value:* dressed(?), $50; nude, $30-$40.

DAM THINGS EST.: 2½in (6cm). Long yellow mohair on head and tail. Green glass eyes. Nude. *Value:* Same as previous troll.

ESKIMO TROLLS

DAM THINGS EST.: 6in (15cm). Long peach colored mohair. Amber glass eyes. Original red felt ties in hair. Clothes are painted on, usually painted in two colors. Very hard vinyl. Marked: "© Dam Things Est. 1964" and "Design Dam" on bottom of feet. These are called *Eskimo* trolls ac-

cording to original advertisement. They are more commonly referred to as *Cheerleaders.* The 2½in (6cm) size are called "mascots." Hard to find in the 6in (15cm) size. *Value:* mint, $75.

DAM THINGS EST.: 2½in (6cm). Long white mohair. Brown glass eyes. Painted on clothing. Marked: "© Dam Things Est. 1964" and "Design Dam" on bottom of feet. Very hard vinyl. *Value:* $15-$20.

DAM THINGS EST.: 2½in (6cm). Long white mohair. Blue glass eyes. Painted on cloth-

ing. He is the *Captain Lightning* character. His felt mask and the lightning bolt on his chest are missing. Marked: "© Dam Things Est. 1964" and "Design Dam" on bottom of feet. *Value:* complete, $35; incomplete, $15-$20.

DAM THINGS EST.: 1½in (4cm). Pencil topper. White mohair and brown eyes. Painted on clothing. Hard vinyl. He is very hard to find. Marked: "© Dam Things Est. 1964" on back. *Value:* $25.

ROYALTY DESIGNS SIT-DOWN TROLLS

ROYALTY DESIGNS *PIXIE*: 2½in (6cm). Long yellow mohair. Green spiral eyes. Black painted eyelashes. Original felt one-piece clothing. Has gold glitter on the felt. Gold hang cord to hang on tree. Marked: "RDF 1968 Fla." on bottom. Hard vinyl. *Value:* $25.

ROYALTY DESIGNS *PIXIE*: 2½in (6cm). Long blue mohair. Blue spiral eyes. Painted black eyelashes. Original felt clothing. Gold hang cord. These are called *Pixie* trolls according to original advertisements. *Value:* $25.

ROYALTY DESIGNS OF FLORIDA: 2½in (6cm). Long red mohair. Green spiral eyes. Black painted eyelashes. Original sheer red top with red ribbon panties stapled on bottom. Marked: "RDF 1968 Fla." on bottom. Hard vinyl. Gold hang cord. *Value:* $25.

ROYALTY DESIGNS OF FLORIDA: 2½in (6cm). Long blue spiral eyes with black painted eyelashes. Original clothes. Marked: "RDF 1968 Fla." on bottom. *Value:* $25.

ROYALTY DESIGNS OF FLORIDA: 2½in (6cm). Long orange mohair. Green spiral eyes. Black painted eyelashes. Original felt clothing. This is a collegiate mascot troll. Gold hang cord. Marked: "RDF 1968 Fla." on bottom. *Value:* $25.

ROYALTY DESIGNS OF FLORIDA: 2½in (6cm). Long pink mohair. Green spiral eyes. Black painted eyelashes. Original felt dress with the words "Me Too" on it. Hard vinyl. Hang cord is missing. Marked. *Value:* $20.

ROYALTY DESIGNS COWGIRL: 2½in (6cm). Long blue mohair. Blue spiral eyes. Black painted eyelashes. Original felt cowgirl outfit. Has a hat that is stapled on; clothing is also stapled on. Marked. Gold hang cord. *Value:* $20.

ROYALTY DESIGNS *LILIPETS*: 2½in (6cm). Long yellow mohair. Green spiral eyes. Black painted eyelashes. Original felt dress with straw hat stapled on. Marked. She also has a red heart sticker on the bottom that reads "©Lilipets." *Value:* $25.

ROYALTY DESIGNS MISCELLANEOUS SIT-DOWN TROLLS

ROYALTY DESIGNS *TINY TIM:* 3¼in (8cm). Black mohair. Bulging plastic eyes. Original clothes, comes with a plastic tulip stapled to one hand and a sign on the other. Sign reads: "Tip toe through the tulips with me." Original heart sticker on bottom reads "Scandia House Enterprises 1965 True Troll." Body is marked: "Roy. Des. Of Fla. 69" on bottom. *Value:* complete, $50; incomplete, $30.

ROYALTY DESIGNS GURU: 3½in (9cm). Long orange and green mohair. Orange mohair comes out of top of head. Green mohair is glued and stapled around body. Bulging plastic eyes. These do not come with clothes. Marked: "RDF 67" on bottom. Original sign stapled to hand reads "Guru the Mediater." Hard vinyl. *Value:* $25-$35.

ROYALTY DESIGNS *TRUE TROLL:* 3½in (9cm). Long pink and white mohair. Pink hair comes out of top of head. White is wrapped around body. Marked: "© Royalty Designs Of Florida 1967." *Value:* $25-$30.

ROYALTY DESIGNS TROLLS

CHICAGO CUB: 3in (8cm). Blue wooly mohair. Plastic eyes. Painted red nose. Smiling face. Original felt baseball uniform with Chicago Cubs pennant glued onto hand. Marked: "© Roy. Des. of Fla. 1969" on back of head. Has brown plastic mitt and baseball glued on hand. Hard vinyl. *Value:* $15-$20.

ROYALTY DESIGNS BASEBALL PLAYERS: All are 3in (8cm) tall. All have mohair. All have plastic eyes. All have original felt baseball uniforms. They all have plastic mitts with baseballs glued to them. They all have felt pennants. Notice that all of the pennants have different baseball terms on them. Also notice the faces of these guys. Those with good terms on their pennants have smiling faces. Those with "foul" and "out" have sad faces. They are marked: "Roy. Des. of Fla. 1969" on the backs of their heads. *Value:* complete set of five, $100; individually, $15-$20.

ROYALTY DESIGNS FARMER: 3in (8cm). White mohair and beard. Plastic eyes. Black painted eyebrows. Red painted nose. Smiling face. Original felt overalls and shirt. Marked: "© Royalty Designs of Florida 1969" on bottom of foot. Hard to find dressed as characters. *Value:* $25.

ROYALTY DESIGNS HOBO BANK: 8in (20cm). Long yellow mohair. Plastic eyes. Molded painted black eyebrows. Red painted nose. Sad face. Original felt clothing. Rope belt is original. Shoes are painted black and are molded to show his toes. Marked: "© Royalty Designs of Fla. 1967" on bottom of foot and back of neck. *Value:* $35-$45.

ROYALTY DESIGNS HOBO: 8in (20cm). Same as previous troll only has orange mohair. *Value:* same as previous troll.

ROYALTY DESIGNS CLOWN: 7in (18cm). Long orange mohair. Plastic eyes. Black painted eyebrows. Red painted mouth and nose. White clown lines above and below eyes. Original felt suit, missing pompon. Marked: "© Roy. Des. of Fla. 1967" on bottom of foot and back of neck. He is a bank. Hard to find. *Value:* $40.

ROYALTY DESIGNS GIRL: 3in (8cm). No hair. Has a red beret stapled to head. Plastic eyes. Black painted eyebrows. Red painted nose. Sad face. Original felt dress. Original container. Came with accessories and extra dress. Marked: "Roy. Des. of Fla. 1968" on back of neck. Hard to find. *Value:* mint in package, $35; loose, $25.

ROOTED HAIR TROLLS

UNMARKED: Both are 7¼in (19cm) tall. Both have long saran rooted hair. Both have orange spiral plastic eyes. The girl has a rooted skirt. They are unmarked. *Value:* pair, $75; boy, $25-$30; girl, $30-$40.

UNMARKED: 7¼in (19cm). Long blonde rooted hair and skirt. Orange spiral eyes rimmed in black. *Value:* $30-$40.

UNEEDA WISHNIK®: 5½in (14cm). Long black mohair. Original flowers in hair. Gray plastic eyes. Brown rooted skirt. Unmarked. *Value:* $30.

UNMARKED: 7in (18cm). Long black rooted curly hair and straight beard. Orange spiral eyes rimmed in black. Hard to find. *Value:* $50.

UNMARKED: 5in (13cm). Silver-blue rooted hair. Two different eye colors. *Value:* two different eye colors, $30; same eye color, $20.

UNMARKED BANKS: 7in (18cm). Long orange rooted hair. Orange eyes. Clothes not original. Horizontal bank slot on back. Soft vinyl. *Value:* $25-$30.

UNMARKED CAVEGIRL BANK: 7in (18cm). Long orange rooted hair. Orange eyes. Original felt cavegirl suit. Unmarked. Soft vinyl. *Value:* $30.

UNMARKED
WISHNIK®:
5½in (14cm).
Long curly lavender rooted hair. Green rhinestone eyes. Original playboy costume. Soft vinyl. Unmarked. *Value:* $35.

WISHNIK®: 5½in (14cm). Long black curly rooted hair. Pink rhinestone eyes. Nude. Marked: "Uneeda Wishnik ™ Patent No#D190-918." *Value:* $25.

HONG KONG: 6½in (17cm). Short blue rooted hair. Blue painted eyes looking downward. Red painted mouth. Painted eyelashes. Original clothes. Cheap plastic body with vinyl head. Marked: "Made in Hong Kong" on back. *Value:* $15.

HONG KONG: 7in (18cm). Long orange rooted hair. Blue painted eyes glancing sideways. Red painted mouth. Painted freckles. Eyelashes. Original red dress with white panties. Marked: "© Holiday Fair Inc. 1967" and "Made in Hong Kong" on back. *Value:* $15.

HONG KONG: 7in (18cm). Green rooted hair. Green painted eyes looking downward. Red painted mouth. Painted eyelashes. Original gold earrings and green felt clothes with silver paper collar with the words "Luva Girl" on it. Marked: "Made in Hong Kong" on back. *Value:* $15.

UNMARKED: 3in (8cm). Black curly rooted hair. Molded brown painted eyes. Dressed in original troll clothing. Tabneck on back of head. *Value:* dressed, $10-$15; nude, $6.
UNMARKED: 2¾in (7cm). Black curly rooted hair. Blue spiral eyes. Nude. Unmarked. *Value:* $6-$9.

REGAL CANADA: 3¾in (10cm). Short brown rooted hair. Molded brown painted eyes. Red painted mouth. Nude. Marked: "Regal Canada" on back. Has five fingers and toes. *Value:* nude, $15; dressed, $20. *Courtesy Lisa Kerner Collection.*

UNMARKED: 2¾in (7cm). Long orange rooted hair. Orange spiral plastic eyes rimmed in black. Unmarked. Original troll clothing. *Value:* $10.
UNMARKED: 2¾in (17cm). Long light blonde rooted hair. Orange spiral eyes. His clothes are airbrushed on. Unmarked. *Value:* $15.
UNMARKED: 2½in (6cm). Long orange-yellow rooted hair. Green spiral eyes. Original troll clothing. Unmarked. *Value:* $10.

44

UNMARKED: 2½in (6cm). Two tones of rooted hair. One is white; the other is purple. Orange spiral eyes. Dressed in original troll clothing. Unmarked. *Value:* dressed, $15; nude, $10.

UNMARKED: 2¼in (7cm). Two-tone rooted hair. One side is orange; the other is white. Dressed in original troll clothing. Unmarked. *Value:* dressed, $15; nude, $10.

UNMARKED: 2¼in (7cm). Three tones of rooted hair. Has red, purple, and lavender hair. Orange spiral eyes. Dressed in original troll clothing. Unmarked. *Value:* dressed, $20; nude, $15.

MOLDED CLOTHING TROLLS

CREATIVE MFG.: 9in (23cm). Hot pink synthetic hair. Orange plastic eyes. Clothes are molded and brushed in light brown wash. She is a cowgirl and is marked: "© Creative Mfg. Inc. 1978" on foot and back of neck. These are banks. *Value:* $30.

CREATIVE MFG. SHERIFF: 9in (23cm). Purple synthetic hair. Orange plastic eyes. Molded sheriff's outfit. Note how his body is a different

mold from the girl's. Marked: "Creative Mfg. Design 1971" on back of head and bottom of foot. These trolls have hard vinyl bodies and heads. Bank slots are on the back. *Value:* $30.

45

CREATIVE MFG.: 9in (23cm). Orange synthetic hair. Orange plastic eyes. Molded caveman outfit. Marked: "© Creative Mfg., Inc. 1978" on right foot. He is a bank also. *Value:* $30.
CREATIVE MFG.: 4in (10cm). Long green synthetic hair. Green plastic eyes. Molded caveman suit. Marked: "© Creative Mfg., Inc. 1976" on foot. Hard to find in this size. *Value:* $20.

MISCELLANEOUS UNUSUAL TROLLS

DAM THINGS EST. CLOWN: 5¼in (15cm). Long salt and pepper mohair. Amber glass eyes. One-piece molded body with painted on clothing. Red painted nose. Marked: "© Dam Things Est. 1964" on bottom of feet. Very rare troll. *Value:* $85-$125.
DAM THINGS EST. PALACE GUARD: 8in (20cm). Black mohair wrapped around vinyl hat. Brown glass eyes. Original felt clothing. Painted gloves and boots. Head is jointed. Marked: "© Dam Things Est. 1965" on bottom of foot. Rare troll. *Value:* $95-$150.

SCANDIA HOUSE ENT.: 11¼in
(29cm). Magenta mohair on head, arms,
and legs. Blue spiral eyes. Blue felt stuffed
body. Arms and legs have wires inside
them so you can pose this troll. Marked:
"J-1" on back of head. Rare troll. *Value:*
$85-$125. *Courtesy of Lisa Kerner Collection.*

ROYALTY DESIGNS OF FLORIDA:
2¾in (7cm). No hair. Green spiral plastic
eyes. Hard molded, painted green vinyl body.
Black felt hat. Marked: "© Roy. Des. of Fla.
1969" on back of neck. Original plastic container. Very hard to find. *Value:* $35.
SWAN MARKED: 3in (8cm). Long orange
mohair. Dark brown eyes. Dressed in original
troll clothing. Soft vinyl. Marked with a triangle
on back, and inside triangle is a swan, with "#9"
beneath the triangle. Has indentations where
fingernails are. Unusual troll. *Value:* $20.

DAM: 2½in (6cm). White wooly mohair. Black
painted eyes. Dressed in original troll clothing.
Very thin rubbery vinyl. One-piece body.
Marked: "De Denmark Dam" on back. *Value:*
$20.
UNMARKED DASHBOARD TROLL:
2¼in (6cm). Orange fun fur hair. Black decal for
pupil on eyes. Hard shiny plastic body. He stands
on a black pedestal. Underneath is a sticky
surface to attach him to a dashboard. He also is
the only troll I have found that has six toes on one
foot and five on the other. He has five fingers on
each hand. Unmarked. *Value:* $20.

R. SHEKTER: 5¼in (13cm). White mohair on head and beard. Brown glass eyes. Very pointy ears and distinctive eyebrows. He is a *Leprechaun*. Original felt jacket and hat. Original gold foil "good luck coin" attached to ribbon on jacket. Body marked: "©R. Shekter 1969, U.K. Reg. Des. Foreign Pats." on bottom. Painted pants and boots. Thin rubbery vinyl. Hard to find. *Value:* $40-$50.

RUSS BERRIE: 4in (10cm). Orange wooly mohair on head and beard. Plastic eyes that move when you move him. Wire glasses. All one-piece yellow vinyl body. Attached ribbon marked: "Timid Soul® © 1966 Russ Berrie & Co. Inc., Fort Lee, N.J." Body is unmarked. He is a very troll-like creature. *Value:* $20.

UNMARKED RUBBER TROLL: 3in (8cm). Long white mohair. Orange eyes. Two painted teeth. Unmarked. Rubber body. Clothes are not original. Her body is curling; the rubber must have been exposed to heat, sun, and humidity. She also has holes for earrings. Hard to find. *Value:* fair condition, $15; mint, $30.

BIJOU TOY INC.: 8in (20cm). Black fun fur hair. Brown painted eyes. One piece soft vinyl body. Original clothes. Marked: "Neanderthal Man 1963" and "© Bijou Toy Inc. 1963" on back of heels and "Neanderthal Man ©" on bottom of foot. *Value:* $30.

MARX TROLLS

LUCKY LOU: Troll is 3in (8cm) tall and has saran hair glued on top of head. He is one-piece vinyl with his hands behind his back. He is very chubby. Unmarked. He came in a leopard skin print box. The box is marked: "Made in the British Crown Colony of Hong Kong. Marx Toys MCMLXIV, © Louis Marx & Co., Inc." Box front reads "Lucky Lou." *Value:* mint in box, $15-$20; loose, $10. *Courtesy of Richard O'Krogly Collection.*

UNMARKED MARX: 3in (8cm). Saran hair glued on top of head. Blue plastic eyes. Nude.

Red painted mouth and black very distinct eyebrows. Molded shoes for feet. Unmarked. *Value:* $10.

UNMARKED MARX: 3in (8cm). Saran hair. Blue eyes. One-piece vinyl troll body. Two painted teeth. Unmarked. *Value:* nude, $10.

UNMARKED MARX: 2½in (6cm). Saran hair. Blue eyes. One painted tooth. I believe these came nude. She is dressed in original troll clothing. Her arms are molded to her sides. Unmarked. *Value:* $15.

RABBIT FUR HEAD TROLLS

UNMARKED: 4in (10cm). Rabbit fur on head and wrapped around body. Cheap thin vinyl head. Brown plastic eyes. Unmarked. Body is hard and stuffed. *Value:* $20. *Courtesy of Lisa Kerner Collection.*

UNMARKED: 3in (8cm). Pink rabbit fur on top of head. The rest of body is rabbit fur. Cheap thin vinyl head with brown eyes. Unmarked. Body is stuffed also. *Value:* $15. *Courtesy of Lisa Kerner Collection.*

UNMARKED: 3in (8cm). Lavender mohair on top of head; rest of body is rabbit fur. Body is

stuffed. Cheap thin vinyl head and brown plastic eyes. Unmarked. *Value:* $10-$15.

UNMARKED: 2in (5cm). Green rabbit fur on top of head. Painted facial features. Has feet but no arms. Rest of body is wrapped in rabbit fur. Had elastic hang cord attached to top of head. Unmarked. *Value:* $15-$20.

KEYCHAINS: Both are 1in (3cm). Both have rabbit fur on top of head and both have beards. Brown plastic eyes. Thin vinyl heads. Keychains attached to tops of heads. Unmarked. *Value:* $3-$6 each.

CHAPTER V
Different Colored Trolls and Monsters

In this chapter, you will see the variety of different colored trolls that were manufactured. You will also see the many monsters, as well as a few Martian trolls, that were available. Black trolls are especially prized by collectors because of the limited number manufactured. Their skin tone is more of a chocolate brown color. There are also truly black colored trolls. Other colors found include red, green, yellow, and white, to name a few.

BLACK TROLLS

THOMAS DAM: 7in (18cm). Black playboy non-bank troll. Yellow mohair and orange eyes. Original false eyelashes. Original black felt bunny ears and suit. White felt collar and cuffs. Hard vinyl. Jointed head. Marked: "Thomas Dam" on back. Very rare. *Value:* $150-$200; nude, $75-$100. *Courtesy of Lisa Kerner Collection.*

SCANDIA HOUSE PLAYBOY: 2¾in (7cm). Black mohair wrapped up in felt bunny ears. Orange spiral eyes. Complete bunny outfit. Original container. Troll unmarked. Made by Scandia House Enterprises in 1965. *Value:* mint in package, $65. *Courtesy of Lisa Kerner Collection.*

SCANDIA HOUSE GROOM: 2¾in (7cm). Red mohair tucked under hat. Orange spiral eyes. Complete tuxedo outfit. Troll unmarked. Original container with red heart sticker. Sticker reads: "#13 Groom for the 'in' Troll." *Value:* mint in package, $65. *Courtesy of Lisa Kerner Collection.*

SCANDIA HOUSE BRIDE: 2¾in (7cm). Red mohair. Orange spiral eyes. Complete bride outfit. Original container. Troll unmarked. Original red heart sticker reads: "© Scandia House Enterprises 1965 True Troll." *Value:* mint in package, $65. *Courtesy of Lisa Kerner Collection.*

SCANDIA HOUSE FOOTBALL: 2¾in (7cm). Yellow mohair tucked under white plastic helmet. Orange spiral eyes. Original felt uniform. Comes with brown plastic football. Original container with red heart sticker, which reads: "#9 FOOTBALL FOR THE 'IN' TROLL." *Value:* mint in package, $65. *Courtesy of Lisa Kerner Collection.*

ROYALTY DESIGNS SIT-DOWN: 3in (8cm). White puffy mohair. Plastic shake eyes. Original outfit. Pearl necklace. Came with accessories and an extra dress. Marked: "Roy. Des. of Fla. 1968" on bottom. First sit-down troll I have seen with shake eyes. *Value:* mint in package, $65.

ROYALTY DESIGNS SIT-DOWN: 3in (8cm). Orange mohair. Green spiral eyes. Nude. Marked: "Roy. Des. of Fla. 68'" on bottom. *Value:* nude, $40.

HONG KONG: 2¼in (7cm). Red rhinestone eyes. White rabbit fur hair. Original clothes. Mouth painted red. Uses the same mold as the Dam *Eskimo* small troll. Marked: "Made in Hong Kong" on back. Plastic body. I believe these are late 1980s issues. *Value:* $20.

GOLLIWOG: 3in (8cm). White rabbit fur on head. Red rhinestone eyes. Red painted mouth. Hard plastic body. Original clothes. Marked: "Hong" on back. *Value:* $25.

UNMARKED: 3in (8cm). White rabbit fur

on head. Blue plastic eyes. Thin plastic body. Jointed head. Unmarked. *Value:* $15-$20.

MISCELLANEOUS COLORED TROLLS

UNMARKED BANK: 7in (18cm). Blue wooly mohair. Green eyes rimmed in black. Soft orange vinyl skin. Large rounded ears. Dressed in original clothes. He is a bank. Unmarked. *Value:* $60.

UNMARKED BANK: 7in (18cm). Red woolly mohair. Orange spiral eyes rimmed in black. He has very pronounced eyebrows. Body is a smooth and shiny vinyl; head has somewhat gritty feel to it. Orange-yellow skin tone. Bank slot is on an angle on the back. Unmarked. *Value:* nude, $40.

MR. LUCKY: 5½in (14cm). Blue woolly mohair. Orange brown spiral eyes. Soft or-

ange vinyl skin. Original foam-like green cave suit. Troll unmarked. Package reads: "Mr. Lucky (copyright pending)." *Value:* mint in package, $40; loose, $30. *Courtesy of Richard O'Krogly Collection.*

UNMARKED: 2¾in (7cm). Long white rooted hair and beard. All one-piece green vinyl skin tone. Molded painted eyes. Unmarked. Tabneck on back. *Value:* $25.

UNMARKED: 2¼in (7cm). Long white rooted hair and beard. Molded painted eyes. All red body. Unmarked. Tabneck on back. *Value:* $25.

UNMARKED: 2¾in (7cm). Long red rooted hair and beard. All white vinyl skin tone. Tabneck

on back. Unmarked. *Value:* $25. *Courtesy of Richard O'Krogly Collection.*

WISHNIK®:
2¼in (7cm). Long pink mohair. Red plastic eyes. Red one-piece vinyl body. He was purchased in this container. Troll is unmarked. *Value:* $25.

UNMARKED DEVIL: 2¼in (7cm). White mohair. Red plastic eyes. All red vinyl body. Dressed as a devil. Unmarked. *Value:* $25.

UNMARKED: 2½in (6cm). Blue wooly mohair. Black pin eyes. Original felt clothes are glued on. Very hard white plastic body. Unmarked. *Value:* $20.

UNMARKED: 3in (8cm). Multi-color synthetic hair. Blue eyes. Raspberry colored vinyl. He is a 1983 issue *Wishnik®*. He is dressed as the *Sport-nik*. Missing bat. Unmarked. *Value:* loose, $12.

UNMARKED: 2¼in (7cm). Black rooted hair. Black painted eyes. All orange one-piece vinyl body. Unmarked. *Value:* $15.

HONG KONG: 5in (13cm). White rabbit fur on top of head. Pearl pinheads are the eyes. Original clothes. All one-piece thin plastic white body. Marked: "Made in Hong Kong" on back of neck. Hard to find. *Value:* $25.

SKATEBOARD TROLL: 3in (8cm). White mohair. Black pinhead eyes. All one-piece very hard plastic green body. He is glued to an all wood yellow skateboard with metal wheels. Unmarked. Hard to find. *Value:* $30.

HONG KONG: 3½in (9cm). Did not come with hair. Painted eyes. All pink plastic body. Has loop on top of head so you can hang him. Marked: "Made in Hong Kong" on back. I believe these trolls were carnival prizes. *Value:* $10.

HONG KONG: 3in (8cm). Plastic "winky" eyes. One-piece cheap plastic blue body. Marked: "Made in Hong Kong." These types of trolls are easily dented. *Value:* $4-$8.

HONG KONG: Same as previous troll but with red body.

HONG KONG: 3in (8cm). Blue plastic eyes. Note his pointy ears. He is fleshtone. Marked: "Made in Hong Kong" on back. *Value:* $4-$8.

MONSTER TROLLS

UNMARKED *FRANKENSTEIN:* 3in (8cm). Long black mohair. Painted facial features. Very hard one-piece green plastic body. Unmarked. Very hard to find. *Value:* $35-$50.

UNMARKED *FRANKENSTEIN:* 3½in (9cm). Molded painted black hair. Painted facial features. Soft white vinyl skin. Head jointed. Unmarked. Very hard to find although the version with mohair is even harder to find. *Value:* $30-$40.

UNMARKED *FRANKENSTEIN:* 3½in (9cm). Molded painted hair. Painted facial

features. Soft green vinyl skin. Unmarked. These *Frankensteins* have very detailed facial features. Head jointed. *Value:* $30-$40.

UNMARKED *KING KONG:* 3½in (9cm). White rabbit fur pasted on top of head. Painted facial features. All black two-piece thin plastic body. He is unmarked. Original clothes. Late 1980s issue. *Value:* $15.

HONG KONG *FRANKEN-STEIN:* 3½in (9cm). Black rabbit fur hair pasted on top of head. Painted facial features. Original clothes. Thin cheap two-piece green body and head. Marked: "Made in Hong Kong" on back. 1980s issue. *Value:* $15.

HONG KONG WEREWOLF: 3¾in (10cm). Black rabbit fur hair pasted on top of head. Painted facial features. Original clothes. Two-piece brown cheap plastic body.

1980s issue. Marked: "Made in Hong Kong" on back. *Value:* $15.

JAPAN VAMPIRE: 3in (8cm). White rabbit fur glued on top of head. Amber plastic eyes. Original clothes. Two-piece cheap plastic orange-red colored body. Marked: "Japan" on back. *Value:* $10-$15.

UNMARKED VAMPIRE: 3in (8cm). White rabbit fur hair glued on top of head. Brown plastic eyes. Fleshtone cheap plastic. Head is jointed. Unmarked. Original clothes. *Value:* $10.

HONG KONG: 3in (8cm). White rabbit fur pasted on top of head. Gold spiral plastic eyes. Painted white fangs and red mouth. Notice how his face and ears differ from those of the other two trolls. His green skin is also a better quality plastic, more rubbery. Marked: "Made in Hong Kong" on back of neck and back. *Value:* $15-$20.

MARTIAN TROLLS

UNMARKED MOON MONSTERS: 6in (15cm). Has long yellow mohair, green glass eyes, original felt clothes, painted eyelids, painted mouth, three fingers per hand and three toes per foot. Unmarked. Hard to find in this size. The next one is the same except for the peach color of her mohair and her different dress color. *Value:* $45-$75.

L. KHEM MOON MONSTERS: 3in (8cm). Long peach colored mohair. Gold spiral eyes. One-piece fleshtone smooth vinyl body. Nude.

Marked: "L. Khem © 1964 Pat. Pend" on bottom of foot. *Value:* $20.

L. KHEM MOON MONSTERS: Both are 3in (8cm) tall. One has green spiral eyes; the other has blue eyes. One has magenta colored mohair; the other has white hair. One has a green body and the other is blue. All of these moon monster trolls have what appears to be a flat peanut on their backs. Marked: "© 1964 L. Khem Pat. Pend." on the bottoms of their feet. *Value:* $25-$40 for the colored body moon monsters.

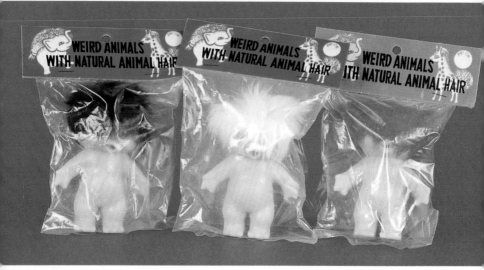

JAPAN: 3in (8cm). All have rabbit fur hair. They come with red, black, and white hair. All have brown plastic eyes. All are thinner vinyl that is fleshtone in color. All are marked "Japan" on the bottoms of their feet. Original poly bag with cardboard header. *Value:* mint in package, $10.

L. KHEM: 3in (8cm). One troll has long magenta colored mohair; the other has pink hair. They both have green spiral plastic eyes. One-piece green vinyl bodies. They have a numeral "8" molded on their bellies; the "8" is painted red. Mouths are painted red also. Marked: "L. Khem 1964. Pat. Pend." on bottoms of feet. Hard to find. *Value:* $40.

REISLER DEVIL TROLLS

REISLER SUCTION CUP: 4in (10cm). Brown rabbit fur hair on head, around waist, and on tail. Clear blue plastic eyes. This is a recent issue. Original plastic red heart tag. Tag is stuck into vinyl body with a metal clip. He is 1/4in (.65cm) smaller than the older models. Marked: "J.N. Reisler. Made in Denmark" on bottom of foot. He has a chain with a suction cup attached so you can hang him up. *Value:* $15-$20.

REISLER: 4in (10cm). Green and black mixed rabbit fur hair on head, around waist, and on end of long tail. Royal blue plastic eyes. Original red heart tag. Marked: "Reisler Made In Denmark J.N." on bottom of foot. He has a chain on top of his head and a long black plastic tail. *Value:* $20.

REISLER: 4¼in (11cm). Yellow rabbit fur with brown tips. Turquoise blue plastic eyes. He has a long rubbery tail with a tuft of hair on the end. Marked: "Reisler Made In Denmark J.N." and "Reisler 1966" on bottom of feet. His cheeks and the tip of his nose are slightly rose colored. The newer ones do not have any face coloring. *Value:* $25-$30.

KEYCHAIN: 1¾in (5cm). Red fun fur glued on top of head. Yellow-orange color plastic eyes. Yellow felt skirt. Hard vinyl body. Can be used as a pencil topper. Marked: "1966 Reisler" on back. He is a recent issue (1989). *Value:* $5-$8

JAPAN: 4in (10cm). White fun fur hair on top of head. He does not have a tail. Large blue plastic eyes. Original hat and collar. Hat has gold hang cord on top. He has red painted cheeks, nose, ears, and mouth. He is made of a thinner brown vinyl. Marked: "NINOHIRA©JAPAN" on bottom of foot. He has four fingers per hand, no horns, and bigger, rounder ears than the Reislers. *Value:* $25.

REISLER GIRL: 3¼in (10cm). White woolly mohair. Blue plastic eyes. Dressed in original felt clothing. Reislers dressed in clothing are harder to find. This troll has no horns; they appear to have been cut off. Marked: "Reisler Made In Denmark, J.N." on bottom of foot. *Value:* $35.

REISLER *SANTA:* 1½in (4cm). This troll is a pencil topper. White fun fur beard. Blue plastic eyes. Dressed as a *Santa*. Also has a pin on the back. Marked: "© 1966 Reisler Made In Denmark" on back. He has no horns. *Value:* $10.

CHAPTER VI
Vinyl Trolls in Original Costumes

Trolls have been manufactured with a wide variety of costumes. This chapter features trolls ranging from 12in (31cm) to 2¾in (7cm) in size. At the conclusion of the chapter, I will show you some of the more common troll outfits. Chapter VII features 3in (8cm) to 2½in (6cm) vinyl trolls in original clothes.

ARMED SERVICES

THOMAS DAM: 7in (18cm). White mohair. Blue eyes. Dressed in original felt clothing with one pocket missing. He represents the Marines. He is not a bank. Marked: "Thomas Dam" on back and "© 1961 190-918 Denmark" on bottom of foot. Hard to find. *Value:* $50-$60.

SCANDIA HOUSE ENT.: 5½in (14cm). Peach colored short mohair. He is a Marine also. Missing a pocket. Marked: "K-1" on back of neck. Purple spiral eyes. *Value:* $30-$40.

UNEEDA WISHNIK®: 5½in (14cm). White mohair. Clear green plastic eyes. One-piece silkscreened Army outfit. He also has a cap. Marked: "Uneeda Wishnik™ Pat. Pend. D190-918" on back. *Value:* $30-$40.

UNMARKED: 2¾in (7cm). Black mohair. Orange plastic eyes. One-piece Army uniform. Troll unmarked. *Value:* $10-$15.

SCANDIA HOUSE ENT.: 5½in (14cm). Magenta colored mohair. Orange spiral eyes. Complete felt sailor uniform. Troll unmarked. *Value:* $30-$40.

UNEEDA *WISHNIK*®: 5½in (14cm). Bright red short mohair. Large amber plastic eyes. He also has a "black eye." Complete one-piece silkscreened sailor uniform. Also has a vinyl sailor cap pinned on back of head. *Wishniks* with oversized eyes are harder to find. *Value:* $50.

SCANDIA HOUSE ENT.: 5½in (14cm). Yellow short mohair. Orange spiral eyes. Complete felt sailor uniform with cap. Troll marked: "K-20" on back of neck and "22" on bottom of foot. Also has original red heart sticker indicating a "True Troll Scandia House Ent. 1965" on back of uniform. *Value:* mint, $45.

UNEEDA *WISHNIK*®: 2¾in (7cm). Long white mohair. Amber plastic eyes. Original one-piece silkscreened sailor uniform. Black shoes. Marked with double horseshoes on bottom of feet. *Value:* $10-$15.

ASTRONAUTS

THOMAS DAM: 7in (18cm). Orange mohair. Green eyes. He is not a bank. Original one-piece silver space suit with helmet. Helmet has plastic face shield. Marked: "Thomas Dam" on back. Very hard to find. *Value:* $65-$75.

SCANDIA HOUSE ENT.: 1½in (4cm). He is a pencil topper. Long purple mohair. Plastic green eyes. Complete silver suit. Pencil is marked: "© Scandia House Enterprises 1966." Troll is marked: "S.H.E. 1964" on back. Original poly bag with cardboard header. *Value:* mint in package, $30; loose, $20.

THOMAS DAM: 5½in (14cm). Lavender mohair. Blue spiral eyes. Original silver space suit. Marked: "Thomas Dam" on back. Hard to find. *Value:* $40-$55.

UNMARKED: 2½in (6cm). Long yellow mohair. Green spiral eyes. Original silver space suit. Has gold hang cord attached to helmet. Unmarked. The most easily found of the trolls dressed in space suits. *Value:* $15-$20.

CAVEMAN

SCANDIA HOUSE ENT.: 5½in (14cm). Purple mohair. Green spiral eyes. Original mohair caveman suit. Original gold paper tooth around neck. Tooth reads "UGH," with "© Scandia House Enterprises 1965" on the back. Troll marked "K 10" on back of neck and "15" on bottom of foot. Also has original red heart sticker on back. *Value:* $35.

SCANDIA HOUSE ENT.: 5½in (14cm). Long white mohair. Green spiral eyes. Original mo-

hair cave suit. She is the mate to the caveman. No tag. Marked "24" on bottom of foot. *Value:* $30.

SCANDIA HOUSE ENT.: 2¾in (7cm). Long peach mohair. She has a gold paper bone in her hair. Green eyes. Mohair cave suit. Gold paper tooth around neck reads "UGHIE UGHIE." Other side of the tooth reads "© Scandia House Enterprises 1965." Troll is unmarked. Original container. *Value:* mint in box, $30; loose, $20.

COMIC BOOK SUPER HEROES

(OPPOSITE PAGE, bottom)

UNMARKED *BATMAN:* 2¾in (7cm). Long blue mohair. Cannot tell eye color. Dressed in one-piece black felt cape with cowl. He is on a cardboard background with white paper on which is the word "Batroll" and a picture of what appears to be a haunted house. This troll is made by SHERI, and the paper with the troll says, "Made in Brooklyn, N.Y. U.S.A." Troll is unmarked. *Value:* $35.

UNMARKED *BATMAN:* 2¾in (7cm). Red fun fur type hair. Green eyes. Original velveteen *Batman* suit. Troll is unmarked. He is the easiest of all *Batman* trolls to find. *Value:* $15-$20.

UNMARKED *BATMAN:* 5in (13cm). White fun fur type hair. Green eyes. Original velveteen *Batman* suit missing bat emblem. Troll is unmarked. Hard to find. *Value:* $45-$50.

RUBBER *BATMAN:* 1½in (4cm). Pencil topper. One-piece molded body. Airbrushed mask and wings. Painted red mouth. Rabbit fur pasted on top of head. He is made of thin rubber. Marked: "Made in Hong Kong" on back of wing. Has a red thread so he can be hung. Hard to find. *Value:* $10-$15.

UNEEDA *WISHNIK®:* 5½in (14cm). Yellow mohair. Large plastic bulging eyes. Complete blue felt two-piece outfit. Costume is silkscreened and is usually found with cowl missing. Marked: "Uneeda Wishnik ™ Patent No. D190-918" on back. *Value:* complete, $65; missing cowl or cape, $40.

PLASTIC *BATMAN:* 1½in (4cm). Pencil topper. Blue rabbit fur on top of head and yellow plastic body. The pencil topper at far right is identical but with white hair and green body. Painted facial features. These were party favors. Marked: "Hong Kong" on back of wings. Hard to find. *Value:* $8-$12.

UNMARKED *BATMAN:* 2½in (6cm). Long brown mohair. Blue spiral eyes. Original complete *Batman* suit. Troll is unmarked. Hard to find in this suit. *Value:* complete, $30.

UNMARKED *ROBIN:* 3in (8cm). Long lavender mohair. Blue spiral eyes. Original felt *Robin* uniform. Even has his "R" emblem. Mask is glued on to face. Hard to find. Troll unmarked. *Value:* complete, $30.

UNEEDA WISHNIK®: 5½in (14cm). White mohair. Gold plastic eyes. Complete one-piece silkscreened *Superman* outfit. Red nylon cape. Marked: "Uneeda Wishnik™ Patent No.#D190-918" on back. Hard to find. *Value:* $65.

UNEEDA WISHNIK®: 5½in (14cm). Pink mohair under mask. Clear gray plastic eyes. Complete green velveteen silkscreened outfit. Marked: "Uneeda Wishnik™ Patent No.#D190-918" on back. He is called *Green Wasp* but is better known as the *Green Hornet* troll. *Value:* $50-$65.

SCANDIA HOUSE ENT.: 5½in (14cm). Long yellow mohair. Purple spiral eyes. Unknown felt uniform. He looks like he may be an unmarked *Robin* or *Robin Hood*. A *Batman* suit was also made in these same colors. Troll came with black

tights also, and I therefore tend to think this is *Robin, Batman's* sidekick. Troll is marked "K 3" on back of neck. *Value:* $45-$50.

DAM THINGS EST.: 6in (15cm). Short white mohair. Amber glass eyes. Painted black body. Uses the same body as the Dam Things Est. *Eskimo* troll. Marked same as the *Eskimo.* He is missing his cape, his mask and the lightning bolt emblem on his chest. Known as *Captain Lightning.* Hard to find. *Value:* complete, $75; as shown, $35.

DAM THINGS EST.: 2¼in (7cm). Long white mohair. Blue glass eyes. He is the smaller Dam Things Est. *Captain Lightning.* His mask and lightning bolt are missing. *Value:* complete, $35; as shown, $15.

BRIDES AND GROOMS

UNEEDA *WISHNIK*®: 5½in (14cm). Long white mohair. Clear gray plastic eyes. Complete original groom outfit. Marked: "Uneeda Wishnik™ Patent No. D190-918" on back. *Value:* $30.

UNEEDA *WISHNIK*®: 5½in (14cm). Long black mohair. Clear gray plastic eyes. Original bridal dress and veil. She carries an original bouquet. She is marked the same as the groom. *Value:* $30.

SCANDIA HOUSE ENT.: 2¾in (7cm). Long green mohair. Green spiral eyes. Original bridal costume. Original red heart paper tag. Troll unmarked. *Value:* $15-$20.

UNEEDA *WISHNIK*®: 3in (8cm). Long blue mohair. Clear gray eyes. Original lace bride's dress and veil. Marked with double horseshoes on bottom of feet. *Value:* $12-$18.

UNEEDA *WISHNIK*®: 3in (8cm). Long yellow mohair. Red plastic eyes. Original felt groom's outfit. Marked: same as bride. *Value:* $12-$18.

THOMAS DAM: All are 7in (18cm). They are not banks. They are dressed in traditional ethnic costumes. All have nice mohair tucked under their hats. Outfits are nicely detailed; notice how each is slightly different. Trolls are marked "Thomas Dam" on their backs. *Value:* $50-$60 each.

SCANDIA HOUSE ENT.: This group is the Scandia House *Chop & Suey* and *Chop Chop* family. The father is 6in (15cm) tall with magenta mohair that is braided in the back. He is missing the original gold paper hat that is marked "Chop." Original satin outfit. The mother is 6in (15cm) tall with peach colored mohair and green eyes. She wears her original white satin outfit but is missing the original gold paper tag necklace marked "Suey." The baby is 2¾in (7cm) tall with blue mohair braided through a gold paper hat that is marked "Chop Chop." He wears his original satin pants. Notice the mother's teardrop pear earrings. *Value:* complete family, $100; separate as shown: 6in (15cm) size, male $30, female $30; baby $20.

SCANDIA HOUSE ENT.: These represent *Eskimos*. The taller troll is 6in (15cm) with blue mohair and orange spiral eyes. The baby is 2¾in (7cm) tall with pink mohair and orange eyes. Both wear white fun fur coats and hats with yellow mohair trim. They are unmarked Scandia House trolls. A 12in (31cm) Dam Things Est. *Eskimo* troll was also made. *Value:* 12in (31cm), $150-$200; 6in (15cm), $40-$55; 3in (8cm), $15-$25.

TROLLS IN VARIOUS COSTUMES

UNEEDA *WISHNIK®:* 8in (20cm). Graduate. White mohair. Orange plastic eyes. Black linen type gown. Missing cap. Probably the easiest outfit to find on trolls. This size troll is hard to find. Marked: "Uneeda Wishnik™ Patent No. D190-918" on back. *Value:* complete, $65; as shown, $45.

UNEEDA *WISHNIK®:* 5½in (14cm). Graduate. Long white mohair. Amber plastic eyes. Complete graduate outfit. The diploma says: "This is to certify that _____ is a genuine Smartnik and is now a fullfledged member of the Wishnik family. Signed _____." This troll is hard to find with an original diploma. You will also find outfits for the 5½in (14cm) size made of felt. Troll marked: "Uneeda Wishnik™ Patent No. D190-918" on back. *Value:* complete as shown, $35.

UNMARKED: 2¾in (7cm). Unmarked Scandia House. Long yellow mohair. Purple eyes. Complete felt graduate outfit. *Value:* $15-$20.

UNEEDA WISHNIK®: 5½in (14cm). Nurse. Complete blue felt outfit. Blue mohair. Gold eyes. Marked: "Uneeda Wishnik™ Patent No. D109-918" on back. *Value:* $25-$30.

THOMAS DAM: 2¼in (7cm). Doctor. White mohair. Brown glass eyes. Original two-piece doctor's uniform. Comes with a plastic cap and stethoscope. Original shoes. Troll marked: "Dam" on back. *Value:* $12-$18.

SCANDIA HOUSE ENT.: 2¼in (7cm). Nurse. White mohair. Green spiral eyes. One-piece white dress uniform. Original hat. Original shoes. Troll unmarked. *Value:* $12-$18.

THOMAS DAM: 7in (18cm). Pirate. He is a bank. Complete uniform. Gold hoop earring. Original bank tag around wrist. Marked: "Thomas Dam" on back. Bank slot on back. Usually found with eye patch missing. Most commonly found character troll. Note that in the Thomas Dam family of trolls, the males have pointy ears and the females have rounded ears. This is true in the 6in (15cm), 7in (18cm), and 8in (20cm) sizes. *Value:* $45.

THOMAS DAM: 7in (18cm). Female Pirate. She is a bank. Complete uniform. Notice that she has two earrings. She is usually found with her pirate hat missing. Marked: "Thomas Dam" on back. I have only found the 7in (18cm) size female and male pirate

with this beautiful red mohair and green eyes. *Value:* $45.

THOMAS DAM: 6in (15cm). Lavender mohair and green glass eyes. Original pirate outfit. If he came with an eyepatch, it is missing. Marked: "Thomas Dam" on back. Hard to find. *Value:* $35-$40.

SCANDIA HOUSE ENT.: 2¼in (7cm). Blue mohair and orange eyes. Original bullfighter clothes. He is dressed in original troll clothes made by House of Ideas. Troll unmarked. *Value:* $15.

SCANDIA HOUSE ENT.: 2¼in (7cm). Blue mohair and orange eyes. Original felt pirate outfit. Original black shoes. Troll unmarked. *Value:* $15.

SCANDIA HOUSE ENT.: 2¾in (7cm). Playboy. Blue mohair wrapped up in black felt bunny ears. Orange eyes. Eyelashes. Complete outfit. Unmarked. *Value:* \$15.

DAM THINGS EST.: 12in (31cm). Playboy. Pink mohair and blue glass eyes. Original eyelashes and complete outfit made of felt. Marked: "Dam Things Est. 1964" on back of head and bottom of foot. *Value:* \$125-\$175.

THOMAS DAM: 6in (15cm). Aqua-colored mohair and blue glass eyes. Original eyelashes and uniform. Missing black felt bow tie. Marked: "Thomas Dam" on back. Hard to find in this size. *Value:* \$45.

SCANDIA HOUSE ENT.: 6in (15cm). Grayish-white mohair. Green spiral eyes. Missing white cuffs on outfit. No eyelashes. Marked: "K 7" on back of head and "10" on bottom of foot. *Value:* as shown, \$30; complete \$45.

THOMAS DAM: 7½in (19cm). *Robin Hood.* He is not a bank. Long black mohair goes past his feet. Green eyes. Original velveteen hat and coat. Green felt pants. Brown felt belt. Comes with leather arrow case. Wood bow. Hard to find. Marked: "Thomas Dam" on back. *Value:* \$65-\$75. *(Also shown on front cover.)*

SCANDIA HOUSE ENT.: 2¾in (7cm). Long yellow mohair and green eyes. Original felt *Robin Hood* costume. Troll unmarked. *Value:* \$15.

SCANDIA HOUSE ENT.: 2¾in (7cm). Green mohair and green eyes. Original *Robin Hood* outfit. Troll unmarked. *Value:* \$15.

UNEEDA *WISHNIK*®: 5½in (14cm). Blue mohair. Green eyes. Original one-piece judge's outfit. He represents the television show "Laugh-In" and has "Here Comes the Judge" written all over his gown. He also comes with a white plastic gavel. Marked: "Uneeda Wishnik™ Patent No. D190-918" on back. His gown is also marked "© UNEEDA DOLL CO. INC. MCMLXVIII." Usually found without gavel. *Value:* complete, $45.

WISHNIK® JUDGE: The double horseshoe mark appears on the left foot. This is the only 5½in (14cm) size *Wishnik* I have found with this marking. *Value:* $50.

WISHNIK: 5½in (14cm). *Sock-It-To-Me* Troll. Yellow mohair. White bulging oversized plastic eyes. Original pink outfit. Has sayings from the television show "Laugh-In" on clothing — for example, "Verry Interesting." Occasionally found with a "black eye." Marked: "Uneeda Wishnik™ Patent No. D190-918" on back. *Value:* $50.

WISHNIK®: 5½in (14cm). Green mohair and green plastic eyes. Original blue one-piece outfit. Outfit has "Tell It Like It Is" written on it. Marked: "Uneeda Wishnik™ Patent No. D190-918" on back. *Value:* $45.

DAM THINGS EST.: 12in (31cm). Long yellow mohair. Blue glass eyes. Original brown felt dress with orange shirt. Troll marked: "© Dam Things Est. 1964" on back of neck and bottom of foot. *Value:* $100-$150.

THOMAS DAM: 6in (15cm). Blonde mohair and blue glass eyes. Original felt dress and shirt. Marked: "Thomas Dam" on back. *Value:* $35.

SCANDIA HOUSE ENT.: 2¾in (7cm). Yellow mohair in original pigtails. Orange eyes. Original felt outfit. Notice how each troll varies slightly. This small one came in an original plastic container not shown. *Value:* mint in box, $20; loose, $15.

THOMAS DAM: 7in (18cm). He is not a bank. Black mohair and blue eyes. Original artist's painted white felt smock. Orange beret. Originally came with a palette. Hard to find. *Value:* $65-$75.

THOMAS DAM: 7in (18cm). Called *Fred Farmer*. He is not a bank. White mohair and blue eyes. Original felt outfit, missing his brown hat. Marked: "Thomas Dam" on back. Hard to find. This troll has a wife whose name is *Mabel*. She is dressed in a similar outfit. *Value:* $50 each.

THOMAS DAM: 7in (18cm). Prom girl. She is not a bank. Aqua-colored mohair. Blue eyes and original eyelashes. Original silvery-metallic dress. Marked: "Thomas Dam" on back. *Value:* $40-$50.

THOMAS DAM: 7in (18cm). Collegiate bank. Yellow mohair. Green eyes. Original felt two-piece sunsuit with the words "Hi" and "U of Florida" on it. Marked: "Thomas Dam" on back. *Value:* $35-$45.

THOMAS DAM: Raincoat banks. Both have yellow mohair and blue eyes. They wear blue vinyl raincoats with matching hats. The girl has white felt underwear, and the boy has blue felt pants. They are marked: "Thomas Dam" on their backs. This color is harder to find; the yellow raincoat banks are much easier to find. It is also very difficult to find the boy with his hat on; nine times out of ten the hat is missing! *Value:* complete pair, $100; individually, $40-$50.

THOMAS DAM: These trolls are the same as previous trolls except that they have orange mohair and green eyes. Both are marked "Thomas Dam." *Value:* $35-$45 each.

68

SCANDIA HOUSE ENT.: 6in (15cm). Fisherman. Green mohair and green eyes. Original felt outfit with plastic straw-like pole with attached felt fish. Hat has been replaced. Unmarked. *Value:* $25-$35.

SCANDIA HOUSE ENT.: 5½in (14cm). Long peach mohair and green eyes. She is dressed in a stretchy purple nylon two-piece suit. Has original paper tag around her neck. She is an unmarked Scandia House Enterprises troll. I believe she is in a skiing outfit. It is a common outfit. *Value:* $25-$30.

SCANDIA HOUSE ENT.: 6in (15cm). Peach mohair and green eyes. Original brown felt cap and uniform. He is unmarked. Hard to find. *Value:* $35-$40.

SCANDIA HOUSE ENT.: 5½in (14cm). Blue mohair and orange eyes. Original one-piece dress. I am not sure if she is a cheerleader or a sailor girl. Marked: "K 3" on back of neck. *Value:* $25-$30.

SCANDIA HOUSE ENT.: 6in (15cm). Clown. Pink mohair and blue eyes. Complete felt clown suit. Has original red paper tag around neck. He is by Scandia House. Usually found with hat missing or pompons off. *Value:* as shown, $30-$40.

SCANDIA HOUSE ENT.: 5½in (14cm). Ballerina. Peach mohair and green eyes. Original felt tutu with felt tiara in hair. Original heart tag around neck. She is by Scandia House. *Value:* as shown, $30-$40.

THOMAS DAM: 5½in (14cm). Valentine girl. Yellow mohair pulled to one side in a ponytail. Blue glass eyes. I bought this from a salesman who worked for Scandia House Enterprises. I was told this was a prototype outfit that was never put on the market. The red heart is glued to the white tutu-type dress. It has a gold arrow with the words "I Love You" on it. Original red sandals glued to feet. Troll marked: "Thomas Dam" on back. *Value:* $75.

SCANDIA HOUSE ENT.: 5½in (14cm). *Mod Maude*. She has black mohair and green eyes. Complete '60s type outfit. She has a mate named *Mod Claude*. He is dressed the same as *Maude* except he wears plaid pants. Marked: "K 8" on back of neck. *Value:* $25-$30.

SCANDIA HOUSE ENT.: 6in (15cm) pair of Scandia House trolls dressed in original matching outfits. She has black mohair and lavender eyes. He has brown short mohair and orange spiral eyes. His outfit is two pieces. *Value:* pair, $60; $25 each.

WISHNIK®: 5½in (14cm). Grandma troll. She has peach mohair and amber eyes. She is dressed in her original outfit, including original plastic glasses. Marked: "Uneeda Wishnik™ Patent No. D190-918" on back. Hard to find. *Value:* $35.

WISHNIK®: 5½in (14cm). White mohair and amber eyes. Dressed in two-piece red velveteen Chinese costume. Marked: "Uneeda Wishnik™ Patent No. D190-918" on back. *Value:* $30.

WISHNIK®: 5½in (14cm). Red mohair and oversized amber plastic eyes. Original pink checkered dress. Usual *Wishnik* mark. Hard to find with the oversized eyes. *Value:* $35.

WISHNIK®: 5½in (14cm). Red mohair and rose colored eyes. Original two-piece velveteen outfit. Usual *Wishnik* mark. *Value:* $25.

THOMAS DAM: Pictured on the left are two Thomas Dam cowboy and cowgirl banks. They are 7in (18cm) tall. Both have blue mohair and blue eyes. Both are dressed in felt outfits. The boy is missing one gun. The girl is missing her hat. Hard to find. *Value:* $50 each.

THOMAS DAM: 7in (18cm). Indian girl bank. Has black mohair which was originally in pigtails. One-piece orange felt outfit. Matching headband. Marked: "Thomas Dam" on back. Green eyes. *Value:* $35.

WISHNIK®: 5½in (14cm). Long green mohair and gold eyes. Original blue velveteen two-piece outfit. Original shawl over shoulder. Missing feather in headband. Usual *Wishnik* mark on back. *Value:* $25.

WISHNIK®: 5½in (14cm). Long black mohair and gray eyes. Original velveteen cowboy suit. Plastic brown belt with guns. Original cowboy hat. Usual *Wishnik* mark on back. *Value:* $25.

UNMARKED: 3in (8cm). Unmarked tabneck dressed in original troll Indian outfit. Notice the papoose has a small printed cardboard troll inside. *Value:* with complete papoose, $15-$18.

SCANDIA HOUSE ENT.: 2¾in (7cm) Unmarked Scandia House troll in original felt sheriff's outfit. *Value:* $12-$15.

EEGEE: These two trolls were made by EEGEE. They look just like the 5½in (14cm) *Wishnik®* trolls. The troll on the left is dressed in an original one-piece red felt heart suit. The other troll has been redressed. They are marked: "EEGEE Patent 190-918" on back. *Value:* dressed in original clothes, $30; redressed, $20.

COMMON OUTFITS

The following are the most commonly found dressed trolls. Values are given both for dressed trolls and nude trolls.

THOMAS DAM: 8in (20cm). Dirty white mohair and dark brown eyes. The darker brown eyes and the thinner, squeezable vinyl are typical of the trolls made for the European market. Their tags are not in English. This size troll is not a bank and is 1in (3cm) taller than trolls manufactured for the American market. Dressed in red felt shirt and yellow shorts. Marked: "T. H. Made in Denmark Thomas Dam" on back. Original tag: "Original Lykketrold fra GJOL * Monsterbeskyttet T.H. Dam Toe GJOL .75 (56-411) GJOL P.R. AABYBRO." *Value:* dressed with tag, $55; nude, $25.

THOMAS DAM: 8in (20cm). Long orange mohair and dark brown glass eyes. Original felt ties in hair. Has original foil tag with same wording as boy's tag. Body marked: "1962 190-918 Denmark" on bottom of foot and "Made in Denmark" on back. *Value:* dressed with tag, $55; nude, $25.

THOMAS DAM: This pair is 8in (20cm) tall. They have black mohair and dark brown eyes and are in original felt clothing. Marked: "USA Foreign Pats Pending Made in Denmark" on back of neck and "Thomas Dam" on back. *Value:* dressed, no tags, $45; nude, $25.

THOMAS DAM: This is a pair of 7in (18cm) banks. Their outfits come in several color combinations. These are the most commonly found 7in (18cm) size trolls. They were manufactured for the American market. The vinyl is much heavier and slightly lighter in color than that of the European style trolls. American market trolls come with different eye colors. Amber is the most common eye color, but trolls with orange and green eyes are also available, and occasionally blue eyes are found. The European trolls

have dark brown eyes. *Value:* mint condition, $30; nude, $15.

THOMAS DAM: 6in (15cm) male and 5½in (14cm) female. Both wear original felt clothes. Both have brown glass eyes. The male is European market. His vinyl is squeezable, with a slightly darker flesh tone. The female is a hard vinyl with lighter skin tone. The male is also slightly bigger than the other Dam male pictured here. These are very commonly found trolls. *Value:* European dressed, $25; nude, $10; American market dressed, $20.

THOMAS DAM: Female is 5½in (14cm) and male is 6in (15cm). Both have brown eyes. Both are dressed in green felt clothes. You will find these felt outfits in yellow, red, and green. Trolls are marked "Thomas Dam" on back. *Value:* dressed, $20 each; nude, $10.

WISHNIK®: 8in (20cm) *Wishniks*. They are dressed as cheerleaders. This is the most common outfit you will find these trolls in. Their clothes are made out of felt. The 8in (20cm) size *Wishniks* are hard to find. *Value:* dressed in original clothes, 8in (20cm) size, $40 each. Not shown: 5½in (14cm) dressed in original clothes, $15-$18; 5½in (14cm) nude, $8-$10; 8in (20cm) nude, $15.

CHAPTER VII
Small Vinyl Trolls in Original Clothes

A wide variety of small trolls dressed in original clothes were manufactured. Most small trolls were sold dressed. Some came in packages; some were nude. Individual outfits for trolls could also be purchased. See Chapter X for further information about clothing. Please note that a 3in (8cm) nude troll has a value of $5 to $8. Millions of trolls of this size were manufactured. Many of these smaller trolls are unmarked and without markings it is impossible to tell who made them.

WISHNIK®: 3in (8cm). These are known as *Groovies*. They were made by Uneeda Doll Company. They have rhinestone eyes and different colors of mohair. Their clothes are one-piece and have silly sayings on them. They are hard to find. *Value:* $15-$20.

DAM: 2¾in (7cm). These are known as *Glamorous Trollettes*. They came in clear hard plastic dome-shaped containers with handles on top. *Trollettes* came in six different dress styles and colors and in assorted hair colors. Those shown here are in purple and red dresses. The hat is original. The glitter on their ears is also original and some have glitter around their necks. They are marked "Dam" on their backs. They have brown glass eyes. Hard to find, and even harder to find in their original containers. *Value:* loose, $15-$20; mint in box, $35.

THOMAS DAM: 2¾in (7cm). The troll on the left has black mohair and brown eyes. Original red and yellow two-piece clown outfit. Original black velveteen glitter mask. Two green pompons on front of suit. Marked: "Dam" on back. The next troll is a Dam also. His outfit is green and yellow. No mask. *Value:* $15 each.

UNMARKED: 3in (8cm) tall. These two trolls are both unmarked. One has red molded painted eyes and red mohair. The other has peach mohair and amber eyes. *Value:* $15 each.

SCANDIA HOUSE ENT.: 2¾in (7cm). Peach mohair and green eyes. Original felt swimming trunks and original scuba gear. Troll is unmarked. *Value:* $15-$18.

SCANDIA HOUSE ENT.: 2¾in (7cm). Brown mohair with blonde streaks. Amber spiral eyes. He is dressed as a *señor*. Straw sombrero with traditional shawl. Shirt and pants and original black sandals. Troll unmarked. *Value:* $15-$18.

THOMAS DAM: 2¾in (7cm). White mohair and brown eyes. Two-piece felt bunny suit. He is unmarked. *Value:* $15.

THOMAS DAM: 2¾in (7cm). Long yellow mohair and purple spiral eyes. Original felt bunny suit. Marked: "Dam" on back. *Value:* $12.

SCANDIA HOUSE ENT.: 2¾in (7cm). These are *Collegiate Trolls* by Scandia House Enterprises. Various shades of mohair and eye colors. They come in three-piece felt outfits and represent different universities and colleges. *Value:* $15 each.

UNMARKED: 3in (8cm). Pink mohair and green eyes. Original green stretchy knit swim trunks. He is glued to a surfboard made out of wood. Troll is unmarked. *Value:* $15-$20.
SCANDIA HOUSE ENT.: 2¾in (7cm). Long blue mohair and amber colored eyes. Original felt bikini. Troll came with plastic blue and white surfboard. She is not glued to it. *Value:* without board, $10; complete, $15-$18.

SCANDIA HOUSE ENT.: 2¾in (7cm). Ice skater. She has peach mohair and green eyes. Original purple stretchy knit one-piece pullover outfit. Original ice skates. Original red heart tag indicating a *True Troll* by Scandia House Enterprises. *Value:* with skates, $18; without skates, $12.

SCANDIA HOUSE ENT.: 2¾in (7cm). Another version of the ice skater. She is an unmarked Scandia House troll. Original one-piece felt dress with a blue felt cap stapled to back of head. The cap does not fit because of the troll's thick, long hair. Original ice skates. *Value:* complete, $20.
SCANDIA HOUSE ENT.: 2¾in (7cm). Another version of the ice skater. You will

also find this clothing used as a ski outfit. Troll is an unmarked Scandia House. Her tag is missing. *Value:* $15.
THOMAS DAM: 2½in (6cm). Peach mohair with brown eyes. She is dressed in a one-piece red shiny dress with a white shawl. Pearls and hat are original. Marked: "Dam" on back. *Value:* complete, $15.

WISHNIK®: 2¾in (7cm). Red mohair and rose colored eyes. Original pink velveteen bow with matching party dress. Marked with double horseshoes on bottom of feet. *Value:* $10-$12.
SCANDIA HOUSE ENT.: 2¾in (7cm). Clown suit. Original two-piece outfit. Matches the 6in (15cm) Scandia House clown. She has yellow mohair and deep blue eyes. *Value:* $10-$12.

THOMAS DAM: 2¾in (7cm). Flower troll. Cute two-piece felt suit. Hat is shaped like a flower. Her black mohair comes through the top. She is marked "Dam" on her back. *Value:* $10.
UNMARKED: 2¾in (7cm). Has long white rooted hair. Orange spiral eyes. Original black leatherette jacket with black pants. Original white hat with black trim. Troll unmarked. *Value:* $12-$15.

THOMAS DAM: 2½in (6cm). Dressed in original "grandpa" outfit made by House of Ideas. Troll is marked "© 64" on back. *Value:* $10.
UNMARKED: 2½in (6cm). Short white and pink streaked fun fur hair. Gold plastic eyes. Beige printed cotton dress and straw hat. Another of the many unmarked trolls. *Value:* $12.
THOMAS DAM: 2½in (6cm). Short wooly mohair. Brown glass eyes. Notice how he ap-

pears to be looking upward. Original two-piece blue felt baseball uniform. Has Indian emblem on front and on hat. Marked: "Dam" on back. *Value:* $15.
UNMARKED: 2¾in (7cm). Hawaiian troll. Original gold trim material hula skirt. Flower glued to hair. Unmarked. Troll has black mohair and orange eyes. She has a whitish-pink hard, rubbery body. *Value:* $12.

78

UNMARKED: Approximately 2½in (6cm). These trolls are unmarked. What is unique about them is that they have red plastic tongues in their mouths. You squeeze their stomachs and out come their tongues. They are dressed in original troll clothing. Hard to find. *Value:* dressed in original clothes, $25; nude, $15-$20.

SCANDIA HOUSE ENT.: 2¾in (7cm). These are two mint Scandia House Enterprises trolls. You could purchase these trolls nude. They both have their original red heart tags around their necks. Their bodies are unmarked. *Value:* with tag, $10 each.

RHINESTONE EYE TROLLS: These are two "oddball" trolls. The one on the left is unmarked; the one on the right is marked "Regd. Des. U.K.NO#904-396 and others" on bottom of foot. They have purple rhinestone eyes and hard vinyl bodies. *Value:* $10 each.

UNMARKED: 3in (8cm). Pencil topper. He is unmarked. Has white mohair and amber plastic eyes. Hard to find. *Value:* dressed, $20; nude, $15.

UNMARKED: 3in (8cm). He is unmarked. Has a red heart airbrushed on chest. Has white mohair and amber eyes. Hard to find. *Value:* $25.

DAM: 2¾in (7cm). Peach colored mohair. Brown glass eyes. Nude. He has a dark vinyl skintone. He is marked "Dam" on his back and has an original gold paper tag around his neck. Tag reads: "Original Lykketrold Thomas Dam Design from Denmark" with "Dam Reg. Design 904395" on other side. *Value:* $25.

PENCIL TOPPERS

S.H.E.: 1½in (4cm). Long, thick mohair tied in ponytail. Green plastic eyes. Original blue felt dress with red ribbon on front. These are designed to go on tops of pencils. Marked: "S.H.E. 1964" on back. Also has pin on back. *Value:* dressed, $15.

S.H.E.: 1½in (4cm). Long, thick yellow mohair and green eyes. Original green felt dress with the initials "E.G.V." on it. She also has a pin on her back. Marked: "S.H.E. 1964" on back. *Value:* dressed, $15.

S.H.E.: 1½in (4cm). These are two nude pencil toppers. They are both marked "S.H.E. 1964" on their backs. *Value:* $5-$9.

CLIP-ON TROLLS

KOALA ME®: 2¼in (7cm). These trolls have synthetic hair that comes in different colors. They come with various eye colors. These trolls clip on to surfaces. They were made in 1982. Each comes with a paper tag that has a story inside. They were made by Inge Dykins Hill, "Mother of the Trolls." The tag also says "Another fine product from the Republic of Korea. All new Materials. Made by KOALA ME® Constant Companions U.S. Pat. No. 3,928,933 OH 9454; PA 553 C 1982 I.T.I.-Hawaii.Inc. Honolulu,Hawaii." I believe there are eight different versions of this troll. Their heads are jointed. *Value:* $5-$10.

JAPAN TROLLS

JAPAN: These trolls are marked "Japan" on their backs. The two on the left are 5in (13cm). The two on the right are 4in (10cm). The one on the far right is 2½in (6cm). They have floss-like hair pasted on top of their heads. Original clothes. They are all made out of a thin vinyl. All have plastic eyes. This type of hair pulls out easily. *Value:* dressed 5in (13cm), $15; dressed 4in (10cm), $10; nude 2½in (6cm), $3.

CHAPTER VIII
Non-Vinyl Trolls

In this chapter you will see trolls made from a number of different materials. Trolls have been made out of wood, latex, glass, metal, chalk, and even from pine cones. I will begin with "nodders"—trolls whose heads wobble when they are moved.

NODDERS

JAPAN ANIMALS: Cow on the left stands 4¾in (12cm) high and is 8in (20cm) long. Has purple rabbit fur hair and brown plastic eyes. Body and head are purple flocked material. The head has a lead neck that attaches to a hoop on the inside. The cow is made out of a pressed cardboard material. Original bell around neck. Original gold paper tag is marked: "Lucky Lady the Purple Cow #CP Dabs Pat Pend. No. 22225." Hard to find. *Value:* with tag, $55.
UNMARKED: 3in (8cm) tall and 7½in (19cm) long. Clear plastic eyes. Purple flocked body and head. Small tuft of purple fun fur hair glued to top of head. Unmarked. Green leatherette collar around neck. *Value:* $25-$35.
UNMARKED: 3in (8cm) tall and 7½in (19cm) long. Clear plastic eyes. Tan flocked body and head. Unmarked. He has a face like that of the Japan lion troll. He does not have a mane. Is he a lion or a dog? I think he is a lion; others will argue he is a dog. I will leave it to the reader to decide which animal this troll represents. *Value:* $25-$35.

JAPAN: 4in (10cm). White synthetic floss hair. Brown plastic eyes. Original tag reads: "Happy Go-Lucky The Good Luck Mascot, Made in Japan." Body unmarked. There is a sticker on the bottom of this troll so that he can be attached to a dashboard. He is made out of a chalk-like composition. These trolls break easily. *Value:* mint in box, $50; loose, $25-$35.

UNMARKED: 4in (10cm). Black floss hair. Brown plastic eyes. He is called "Lucky." Body is unmarked. Notice his head and body are slightly different from those of the other troll. *Value:* $25-$35.

BERRIES NODDERS: 5in (13cm). These are nodders made by Berries in 1971 and 1972. They were made in Hong Kong. They have orange plastic eyes. They are a molded vinyl which is painted. All are nicely detailed. The troll on the left is a devil. Base reads: "Have a helluva nice day." She has orange rabbit fur hair. She is marked: "Berries 19©72 Made in Hong Kong #283." The next troll is a doctor. Black rabbit fur hair. Marked: "#262 Berries 1972 Hong Kong." Clipboard reads: "Get well soon." Next we have the "World's Best Secretary." She has black synthetic hair. She is marked "Berries © 1972 Made in Hong Kong." On the right is a "Happy Birthday" troll. He has black rabbit fur hair on his head and as a goatee. Marked: "Berries © 1972 Made in Hong Kong" on bottom. *Value:* if head nods, $20-$30; if broken, $15.

BERRIES NODDERS: On the left is another version of the devil nodder. She has black rabbit fur hair. Next is "I Love You This Much." She has black synthetic hair and is marked "1972 © Hong Kong Berries." The third troll says "We Need Each Other" and is marked: "© 1972 Berries Hong Kong." She has black synthetic hair. The troll on the right carries a sign that says, "Dirty old men need love too." Has black rabbit fur hair on top of head and as beard. He is marked "© 1971 Made In Hong Kong No #280 Berries." *Value:* if head nods, $20-$30; if broken, $15.

HEICO® COUPLE: 9in (23cm). Female (left) has synthetic salt and pepper hair. Brown plastic eyes. Nicely detailed molded vinyl face and body. Clothes and facial features are airbrushed. Original chain wrist tag. Body marked "Heico" on bottom. Male has salt and pepper hair and brown plastic spiral eyes. He is marked "Heico®" on bottom. *Value:* $35-$45 each.

STREGA: 9in (23cm) tall. Has polka dot scarf tied around head. Black hair. Original chain wrist tag. Tag is marked: "Orig. R WESTERN GERMANY." Body unmarked. Sticker on bottom marked "STREGA." She is sitting on a stump. Smaller troll is 6in (15cm) tall. Her scarf is missing. She is marked "Heico®" on bottom. *Value:* large troll, $35-$45; small troll, $25-$30.

HEINZ: 8in (20cm). Black synthetic hair on top of head and as beard. Brown eyes. Carries a stick. Marked: "© Heinz & Co. 1967" on bottom. Original chain metal tag. Older models have metal tags; newer ones have gold foil tags. *Value:* $50-$60.
HEICO®: 9½in (24cm). Salt and pepper hair. One brown plastic eye. She carries a broom. Marked: "Heico®" on bottom. *Value:* $35-$45.

HEICO® BARMAIDS: Troll on left is 9½in (24cm) tall. The one on the right is 5½in (14cm) tall. Both have orange synthetic hair and brown eyes. Original chain tags around neck. Both are marked "Heico®" on bottom. *Value:* large troll, $35-$45; small troll, $25-$30.

A/S NYFORM TROLLS

The following trolls are made in Norway. They are made out of latex. As they age, the latex gets hard and takes on a scaly feel. I suggest keeping these trolls out of sunlight. They are imported by Berquist Imports and are available in Scandinavian shops. The older ones have metal tags with their art numbers stamped on the back. They are designed by Trygve Torgersen in the traditional look of the trolls found in Norwegian folklore.

NYFORM: This is an old man sitting on a stump. He has brown glass eyes. Original orange label tells the story of these trolls. White mohair on top of head. *Value:* still available.

NYFORM: 7½in (19cm). This troll has his original metal tag. Salt and pepper mohair and brown eyes. His tag is "Art No.#702." No longer available. *Value:* $40-$50.

NYFORM: 7in (18cm). Troll is sitting on a stump. Has molded painted hair. Original metal tag around neck. He is "Art No.#110." No longer available. *Value:* $50-$60.

NYFORM COUPLE: Male is 10in (25cm) tall and has salt and pepper mohair. Brown glass eyes. Original metal tag. He is "Art No.#700." No longer available. Female is 9in (23cm) tall and has white mohair with gray mixed in. She has original metal tag. She is "Art No.#701." She is no longer available. *Value:* $65 each.

NYFORM COUPLE: 10in (25cm). Couple is molded standing side by side. She has white mohair and he has synthetic black short hair. They have brown eyes. *Value:* still available.

NYFORM COUPLE: Male is 6½in (16cm) tall with salt and pepper mohair. Brown glass eyes. Original metal tag. He is "Art No.#124." He is still available, but because the troll pictured is an older one, his value is $40. The female is 6in (15cm) tall with white mohair. She has brown glass eyes. Original metal tag. She is "Art No.#114." She carries a stick. Also has a bright orange sticker on bottom marked: "A/S Nyform Tynset Norway/Guarantee." No longer available. *Value:* $45.

NYFORM MAN: 9½in (24cm). Dirty peach colored mohair and large brown glass eyes. He carries a stick. Has a tail, but this troll's tail is broken. *Value:* still available.

UNMARKED: 9in (23cm). He has synthetic black hair. Brown glass eyes. He is not made out of latex. He is unmarked. He looks just like one of the A/S Nyform trolls. He is made out of a hard vinyl material. He also carries a stick. The latex style of this troll is still available. *Value:* for vinyl version, $50-$60.

NYFORM: 8in (20cm). Has short synthetic black hair on head and forming a skirt around waist. Original metal tag. He is "Art No.#121." No longer available. *Value:* $50.

NYFORM SKI-ERS: Troll on the left is still available. His skis are made out of latex also. He has brown eyes and synthetic hair. The troll on the right is no longer available. He is 11½in (29cm) tall. Has brown eyes and synthetic hair. His skis are also latex. He wears a fake fur one-piece tunic style outfit. Poles are sticks. *Value:* with skis, $85.

KOREAN: 4½in (11cm). A/S Nyform look-alike suction cup trolls. These are a smaller version of the Nyform doubleheaded troll. They have brown synthetic short hair and plastic amber eyes. Marked: "Made in Korea" on a gold sticker on bottom. Trolls are unmarked. My husband bought these at a gas station about six years ago. *Value:* $6 each; on display card with six trolls, $45.

KRAGE COUPLE: Both 5in (13cm) tall. Both have orange synthetic hair. Airbrushed bodies and painted facial features. Boy is sitting. One-piece vinyl bodies. Boy marked: "63/605 R"; girl marked: "63/606" on bottom. Both have original paper labels. *Value:* still available.

SYVESTRI BROS. BANK: 20in (51cm). He is airbrushed with blue eyes. He is a bank with a slot in back on his hair. He is made out of chalk. Marked: "Syvestri Bros. Co. 1964" on back. He is very rare. A cement garden fixture was also made using this same mold. It too is very rare. *Value:* bank, $100; garden fixture, $150.

UNMARKED GARDEN TROLL: This is a plastic garden troll. He is 12½in (32cm) tall with airbrushed painting. He is unmarked. Hard to find. *Value:* $35-$45.

PINE CONE TROLL: 7½in (19cm). Has a rubbery molded face. Feet are black painted cardboard. Wire arms are covered with red straw. Troll's body is a pine cone. Marked: "Made in Sweden." Hair resembles dried grass. *Value:* $20-$25.

UNMARKED BAR TROLL: 5½in (14cm) tall troll with orange synthetic hair. Painted facial features. Hard plastic head and hands. Iron body with blue felt coat pasted on back. Plastic brown shoes. He comes with a corkscrew and a bottle opener. He is unmarked. *Value:* $20.

GLASS TROLLS: These are glass trolls from Sweden. They are unmarked but come with a blue sticker which is marked "Bergoala Sweden." They are, from the left: 4in (10cm), 3in (8cm), 3in (8cm), and 1¾in (5cm). The second from the left is blue glass. *Value:* still available.

PEWTER TROLLS: This is a group of pewter trolls. The one on the left is an old woman carrying a water bucket. She is marked: "STOPT TINN PEWTER" on the bottom of her bucket and the bottom of her feet. She is 3in (8cm) tall. Next to her is a troll carrying a club. He is 4in (10cm) tall. Marked: "PARTHA PEWTER PP 260" on bottom. The smaller version is 2½in (6cm) tall. He is marked: "PARTHA PEWTER © 198(?)." I

cannot read the year marked. On the right is a Norwegian pewter troll marked: "Norge" on the front of its base. He is 1½in (4cm) tall. *Value:* still available.

FINLAND: 6in (15cm). Green mohair on head and on tail. Blue plastic eyes. Original dress. Leather hands and feet. Face is made out of pressed paper. Wire body is covered in sheared mohair. Tag on tail is marked: "Himmi Handmade Aleller Tauni Finland." These are very unusual trolls. I believe they are early 1950s. *Value:* $50. *Courtesy of Lisa Kerner Collection.* Boy is 8in (20cm) tall with brown mohair on head and tail. He has blue glass eyes. Original clothes. Leather hands and feet. Pressed paper face. His ears are leather also. Tag marked: "Exclusively An IMC Imports, Ki-made." *Value:* $50.

UNMARKED: Girl is 8in (20cm) tall and has white mohair on head and tail. Blue eyes. Original clothes. Leather hands, feet, and ears. Unmarked. *Value:* $50.

SMOKEY MOUNTAIN TROLLS: These are *Smokey Mountain Trolls.* They are made out of all natural materials. They are stamped "The Arensbak Troll" on their bottom. The one on the left is 11½in (29cm). He has a loop made out of grasses for use in hanging him on the wall. He is also stamped "© 1978" on the bottom. The other two are troll babies. The one on the right is marked. The one in the middle is not. These are made in Tennessee. *Value:* still available.

WHISKEY DECANTERS:
These two trolls are bisque whiskey decanters. The female is 11in (28cm) tall. The top of her head is where the decanter opens. She is marked: "© Alpha, Ind. 1978" on the bottom. The male is 10in (25cm) tall. He is unmarked and has a gold foil sticker marked "Genuine Royal Crown Porcelain." She is empty; he is full. Very hard to find. *Value:* $65 each.

KRAGE-NORGE: 5in (13cm). Made out of porcelain. Marked: "Krage-Norge #12765" on bottom. *Value:* $20.
BISQUE: 5in (13cm). Bisque. Unmarked. *Value:* $20.
CERAMIC: 6in (15cm). Made out of clay. He holds his tail. Marked: "Made in Denmark by Kesa." *Value:* $20.

CHALK: 10in (25cm). Has green plastic eyes. Black rabbit fur hair on top of head. She is cooking over a caldron. She is made out of chalk with airbrushing. Marked: "Figor Runst A/S Hawkete Norway" on bottom. *Value:* $35.
CHALK: 7in (18cm). Has one green eye; the other eye is closed. Molded painted hair. He is made out of chalk with airbrushed features. He is unmarked. *Value:* $30.
CHALK: 6in (15cm). Has green plastic eyes. He has white short mohair glued to top of head. Marked: "Made in Norway" on bottom. He is made out of chalk. These trolls are hard to find because they break easily. *Value:* $30.

WOODEN TROLLS

UNMARKED BANK: 6½in (17cm). Has gray mohair on top of head. Painted facial features. He is a bank. His clothing is glued on. He carries a sign which reads "Telefon-Trollet." He has a wooden backpack with a bank slot on top and a wooden stopper on the bottom. Unmarked. *Value:* $30.
UNMARKED CANDLESTICK: 6½in (17cm). Has black rabbit fur on top of head. He is all wood. Unmarked. Clothes are glued on. He is sitting on a stump. He has a hole in his back to hold a candle. *Value:* $20.

SWEDEN: 15in (38cm). Has long gray mohair covering his head and most of his body. He also has a rope tail with a big tuft of mohair on the its end. Painted facial features. He is made out of wood and has a huge nose. Marked: "981802 Made in Sweden." Sticker on bottom marked: "IB-BO-SVENSK KONSTHANTVERK Made in Sweden." He is the largest wooden troll I have seen. *Value:* $75.
SWEDEN: 4in (10cm). Covered completely in orange mohair. He has a wooden nose, eyes, and feet. Marked: "Sweden" on bottom. *Value:* $20.
KLUTZ: 4in (10cm). Covered completely with yellow and brown mohair. He is just a head. He has wooden eyes and nose. He is unmarked. He has a spring attached to his head; on the end of the spring is a sticker so he can be hung up. Comes in a box marked: "KLUTZ © 1971 Executive Games Inc., Boston Mass. 02124." *Value:* mint in box, $30.

UNMARKED BANK: 8¾in (22cm). Has orange mohair on top of his head. He is a bank. Airbrushed clothing on all wood body. His arms move and he is on wheels. Bank slot on back. Unmarked. *Value:* $25.

SWEDEN: 5½in (14cm). Girl carrying jug. Missing one ear. Black rabbit fur hair. Painted clothes. All wood. Marked: "Made in Sweden" on bottom. Arms move. *Value:* $20.

SWEDEN: 4½in (12cm). Has raccoon fur for hair. Painted facial features. Glued on trim for clothes. All wood. Marked: "Made in Sweden" on bottom of foot. *Value:* $15-$18.

SWEDEN: 4½in (12cm). Has dried grass-like hair. All wood. Stained green body. Marked: "Original Ljungstroms of Sweden Handmade #781" on bottom of feet. *Value:* $10.

SWEDEN: 3½in (9cm). Has gray yarn hair. Earrings are attached to hair. All wood. Green painted body. Original tag marked: "Original Buttickr of Sweden Handmade." Body marked: "Made in Sweden." *Value:* $10.

SWEDEN: 4½in (12cm). Wood troll in original box. Has dirty blonde curly mohair. Blue rope arms and tail. Gray painted body with red skirt. Troll marked: "A V E B E STOCKHOLM." Original tag comes with a story about King Gustav. Container is made out of thin plastic. *Value:* mint in box, $20.

SWEDEN: 4in (10cm). Has gray mohair on top of head. All wood. Paper tag on bottom marked: "Made in Sweden." *Value:* $8-$10.

FINLAND: 3in (8cm). Leather covered stuffed

body. Wood head. Painted facial features. Yellow mohair. Marked: "Finnish Handwork" on bottom of feet. *Value:* $15.

SWEDEN: 4½in (12cm). Has dirty blonde mohair. All wood. Suede glued on clothes. Rope arms. Marked: "Richard Meccrim Per 5 Sweden" on bottom. *Value:* $10-$12.
SWEDEN: 3¼in (10cm). Has black mohair. All wood. Suede clothes. Rope arms. Sticker on belly marked: "Lots A Luck." Troll marked: "#5" on bottom. *Value:* $10.
UNMARKED: 4in (10cm). Has yellow mohair. All wood painted body. Unmarked. Rope arms. *Value:* $10.

SWEDEN PAIR: 3½in (9cm). Both have black yarn hair. They are all wood and dressed in burlap. They have rope tails. Marked: "Made in Sweden" on bottom of feet. They also have copper bracelets on each arm. *Value:* pair, $30.
SWEDEN: 2½in (6cm). Has gray mohair. All wood. Painted on clothing. Yarn tail. One earring missing. Marked: "BLEMSLOJDEN BORES SWEDEN" on bottom of foot. *Value:* $15.
KELLOGG: 2½in (6cm) tall with brown fun fur hair. Pink felt ears. Painted facial features. Brown fun fur clothes. All wood body. Has a sticker on the bottom marked: "© 1972 KELLOGG CO." These were mail-in premiums. I think he is a caveman but he certainly looks like a troll. *Value:* $5.

NORWAY: 6in (15cm). All handcarved Norwegian troll. Lightly stained clothes. He is in a walking pose and carries a stick. Marked: "Made in Norway #830" on bottom of feet. *Value:* $45-$50.

NORWAY: 6½in (17cm) tall. Old woman troll. She is lightly stained handcarved wood.

Marked: "Made in Norway" on bottom. *Value:* $45-$50.

NORWAY: 2½in (6cm) handcarved troll in boat. His oars are missing. He is marked but the mark is unreadable. *Value:* $20.

NORWAY: 5½in (14cm). Handcarved man troll. Lightly stained wood. He holds his tail. Marked: "Made in Norway" on bottom. *Value:* $45.

NORWAY: 5½in (14cm). Handcarved woman troll. Her eyes are closed and she is

also lightly stained. Marked: "Made in Norway" on bottom. *Value:* $45.

NORWAY: 6in (15cm) tall with painted crown on top. This troll is holding his tail. Handcarved lightly stained wood. Marked: "Made in Norway" on bottom. *Value:* $40.

95

NORWAY: 4in (10cm). Old woman troll. Handcarved wood. Very long nose. Marked: "Made in Norway" on bottom. *Value:* $30. **UNMARKED:** 4in (10cm). Red painted cap. Handcarved wood. He is unmarked. I believe he is a *Henning Troll*. They are stamped on the bottom and over time the mark fades. You can still buy these trolls in Scandinavian shops. *Value:* $35.

UNMARKED: 3in (8cm) tall girl with mushroom cap for a hat. Closed eyes. Unmarked. Handcarved wood. *Value:* $25.
NORWAY: 3½in (9cm) tall boy. Lightly stained handcarved wood. Marked: "Made by hand Norway" on bottom. He is in a sitting position. *Value:* $35.

CANDLEHOLDER: 7½in (19cm). Handcarved stained wood. Can be hung on the wall. He is also a candleholder. Marked: "#820" on bottom. *Value:* $45-$55.
HENNING: 6½in (17cm) Handcarved stained troll. Marked: "#152 Henning Carved by hand Norway" on bottom. *Value:* $45-$50.
UNMARKED: 3in (8cm). With his hat he is 10½in (27cm) tall. Handcarved lightly stained wood. He is unmarked. Hat is made out of felt. *Value:* $30.

CHAPTER IX
Displays and Advertising

This chapter presents samples of original store displays and sales brochures. These items are hard to find and, when found, are expensive. Most store displays are discarded after merchandise is sold. Brochures and catalogs also are discarded when merchandise is no longer desirable. It is exciting to find old sales brochures and to see the wholesale prices listed in the 1960s.

DISPLAYS

NAK-NIK OUTFITS: Display is 16in (41cm) x 20in (51cm). It features eight *Wishnik*® trolls dressed in various outfits that were manufactured by the Totsy Manufacturing Company. The names of the outfits are shown under each troll. Today, 30 years later, Totsy is once again making clothes for trolls. *Value:* $200.

WISHNIK® COUNTER DISPLAY: This is a *Wishnik* store counter display. It measures 15in (38cm) x 8½in (22cm). It is 3½in (9cm) deep. It is made out of heavy printed cardboard. It resembles the inside of a church. There are wedding bells on the ceiling inside (not shown). Front of display says "Wishnik Family, © 1964 Uneeda Doll Co. Inc." This display contains two 5½in (14cm) trolls and one 3in (8cm) troll. I find the selection of trolls amusing. The back of the display describes the *Wishniks* that were available. *Value:* $150+. *Courtesy of Richard O'Krogly Collection.*

WISHNIK® COUNTER DISPLAY: This *Wishnik* counter display features the 1982 issue 3in (8cm) trolls. When I bought this, it included six of the twelve different trolls available. The display measures 20in (51cm) x 20in (51cm). *Value:* with trolls, $100.

(Right)

TROLL PINS: This display features twelve 1¼in (5cm) tall gold-tone metal pins on a hard cardboard counter display. The display has a stand on its back like stands used on picture frames. Trolls are unmarked. Display is 10in (25cm) x 12in (31cm). Marked: "Criterion." *Value:* $125+.

(Below)

***BAT-NIK* CLUB:** This is a thin paper display. It measures 8in (20cm) x 6in (15cm). Maker unknown; the display shows only a logo with an Indian riding a horse. On the right is a *Bat-Nik* plastic charm troll. The display features instructions on how to attach the wings. Probably from the early 1960s. *Value:* display, $20; *Bat-Nik* mint in package, $5.

99

DAM THINGS BROCHURE: This pictures shows the front of an original sales brochure featuring the line of Dam Things trolls. It introduces us to the "new" *Iggynormus Trolls*. The trolls were manufactured by Royalty Designs of Florida, the only official licensee for Dam Things *Original Trolls*. The back of the brochure explains how to order and lists prices. The wholesale price listed for one dozen large elephants was $24! *Value:* brochure, $20.

SCANDIA HOUSE BROCHURE: Top of photo shows original color card featuring *New True Horoscope Trolls* by Scandia House Enterprises. Card is 8¾in (22cm) x 3½in (9cm). The back features ordering information and wholesale prices. The minimum order was three dozen and the price was $13.20 a dozen! The card also tells us that Scandia House Enterprises Incorporated was a division of Royalty Designs of Florida Incorporated. *Value:* $10.

SCANDIA HOUSE BROCHURE: Bottom of photo shows the Scandia House Enterprises line of *Collegiate Trolls*. This card opens and provides ordering information and wholesale prices inside. Again the minimum order was three dozen. The price was $12 a dozen! *Value:* $10.

SCANDIA HOUSE ORDER SHEET: Here is an 8in (20cm) x 10in (25cm) color sheet featuring the Christmas line of trolls from Scandia House Enterprises. The sheet features the 13in (33cm), 8in (20cm), 5in (13cm), and 2½in (6cm) *Santa* trolls. Also featured are 1½in (4cm) *Santa* pins and *Angel* pins, the *Pixie* sit-down trolls and *Snow Puss* on

skies. (I have never seen one of the *Snow Pusses*.) One had to order a minimum of three dozen pins. Imagine being able to buy a dozen 13in (33cm) *Santas* for $60!!! *Value:* $15.

Photo on right is an 8in (20cm) x 10in (25cm)

glossy showing various sizes of Dam trolls in different outfits with their wholesale prices. The trolls have original red heart stickers showing they were from Scandia House Enterprises Incorporated. *Value:* $15.

NEWS RELEASE

This is a news release dated February 19, 1966, featuring Inge Dykins and Thomas Dam, who were known as "the mother and father of trolls." Inge Dykins represented Scandia House Enterprises Incorporated, and Thomas Dam represented Dam Things Est. The release explains how they joined forces after all litigations were settled. The release also mentions Robert Shekter was no longer associated with Dam Things Est. According to the release, all patents, copyrights, and trademarks for the original troll dolls in the United States of America were assigned to Scandia House Enterprises. Royalty Designs of Florida was to continue to manufacture the troll dolls as a nonexclusive licensee. This release contains the only information I could find on these companies. I especially enjoy the fact that this release shows us what these people looked like and that it shows us Thomas Dam signing the agreement with a S.H.E. pencil top troll! *Value:* $15.

CHAPTER X
Troll Clothes and Houses
CLOTHES

SCANDIA HOUSE ENT.: This picture shows outfits made for 6in (15cm) Scandia House trolls. The outfits are made of felt. Featured are the *Cowgirl* and *Cowboy*. The *Cowboy's* outfit came with two guns. The other two outfits are for girl trolls. One seems to be a shorts set and the other appears to be a "Sunday best" dress. Both came with straw hats and purses. The shorts outfit came with sunglasses. I love the way costumes were packaged with 6in (15cm) cardboard trolls modeling the outfits! Original poly bag with header reading, "True Troll Fashions, © Scandia House Enterprises, Inc. 1965, fitting all 5in (13cm) trolls." These outfits are hard to find in this size. *Value:* $20-$25 each.

SCANDIA HOUSE ENT.: The outfit on the left is made by Scandia House. It is for 2½in (6cm) trolls. Notice the red heart sticker. The outfit on the right is made by House of Ideas, a company based in Illinois. Their outfits are made out of felt. Original poly bag with header. *Value:* $6-$8 each.

HOUSE OF IDEAS: Manufactured by House of Ideas, these are called *Troll Fads.* Notice the different packaging used. Clothes are made out of felt. Shown here are the *Grandpa, Bikini* and *Minnie Ha-Ha* outfits. On the back of these packages is a listing of all outfits available. House of Ideas even carried a "Nap-Sak" and "Twin Nap-Sak," which were described as "a bunting to carry your troll and wardrobe in." The package is marked: "S.H.E. © 1965." *Value:* $12-$15 each.

BUNALLAN: These outfits made by Bunallan Inc., of California, are called, *Trogs for Trolls.* The package says, "Fits all 2½in (6cm) Supernatural Creatures." Clothes are made out of felt and some come with accessories. The names of the outfits are on the tops of the packages. *Value:* $12-$15 each.

TOTSY: This is another group of clothes manufactured by Totsy. Notice the different packaging. Nice quality clothing with accessories. These are the easiest outfits to find. *Value:* $12.

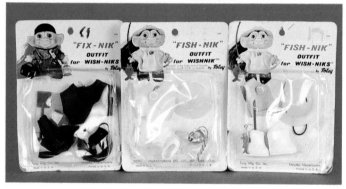

TOTSY: These clothes were made by Totsy Manufacturing Company Inc., of Massachusetts, a company that is now once again, approximately 30 years later, making clothes for trolls. Shown are *Fix-Nik* and *Fish-Nik* outfits. Notice the differences in the two *Fish-Nik* outfits. The raincoats are made of vinyl. Totsy used different types of materials for their outfits. Their outfits also come with accessories. I like the way Totsy featured a picture of a troll wearing the outfit on the package. *Value:* $12-$15.

(Left)

ARCADIA MILLS: These were made by the Arcadia Mills Company, based in Pennsylvania. They called their clothes *Troll Togs*. Original poly bag with header. A cut-out troll models the clothes. The clothes are stretch knits for 2½in (6cm) trolls. *Value:* $10.

TOTSY: Here are more clothes made by Totsy. Notice the different packaging used. The front of these packages list the outfits that were available. *Value:* $12-$15.

TOTSY: Here is yet another different type of packaging used by Totsy. These are known as *Nak-Nik* outfits. Shown here is the sailor's outfit. *Value:* $12.

SHILLMAN: These are called *Troll-Niks*. They are manufactured by Shillman. This outfit is called *Badman*. Nicely illustrated package. Hard to find. *Value:* $15.

BUNALLAN: This is another sample of different packaging used by Bunallan Inc. *Value:* $12.

McCALL'S: Shown are two patterns made by McCall's. *Value:* uncut, $10; cut, $5.

IDEAL: This is a troll house called *Shanty Shack* made by Ideal Toy Corporation. It is covered, printed vinyl with molded plastic furniture inside. Shown are front and back views. Ideal made two different interiors for this house. Plastic handle on top. *Value:* $35.

IDEAL: Shown is the inside of the *Shanty Shack.* Its two rooms consist of a bedroom with bunk beds and a room that is a combination front room/kitchen. A troll picture hangs in the bedroom.

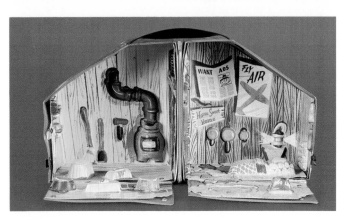

IDEAL: This is the inside of the other version of the *Shanty Shack.* It also has two rooms, a bedroom and a kitchen with a dining area.

STANDARD PLASTICS: The house on the left is the easiest troll house to find. It is made by Standard Plastics Products, Inc. Marked: "U.S. Pat. No.# 3,128,420." It is simply called *Troll House*. It looks like a cave on the outside. Inside it has molded plastic furniture. Has a plastic handle on top which is usually missing. *Value:* with handle, $20; missing handle, $10.

IDEAL STIK SHACK: Ideal made this bamboo style hut called *Stik Shack*. When opened, it converts into a two-story house. It has molded plastic furniture on the inside. The *Stik Shack* is shown here opened. Original paper tag is marked: "Troll Stik Shack Ideal #8F-11-6." Hard to find. It has a bamboo handle. *Value:* mint with tag, $50.

TROLL MANOR: Shown on the left is the *Troll Manor* made by Mattel. It is a cottage style house with a thatched roof. It is molded plastic and the door does not open. Trolls are placed in the house from the side. The house is done in true 1960s style with wild colors and flowered walls on the inside. It is marked: "1966 Standard Plastics Products, Inc. A subsidiary of Mattel, Inc." on the side. Has a blue rope handle. Very hard to find. *Value:* $40.

TROLL HOUSE: Shown on the right is the *Troll House* by Mattel. It is made of plastic. Has a clear "window" in the front so that the inside can be seen. House is shaped like a log. It is marked: "1966 Mattel." Very rare. *Value:* $40.

UNMARKED WOOD HOUSE: The house on the left is unmarked. It is made out of wood. It says: "Troll Houze." Hard to find. *Value:* $35-$45.

DEE DEE DESIGNS: House on the right is an unusual wooden troll house. It has an original paper label and is painted to resemble a cottage. The house opens at the front and has painted mushrooms on the inside. It is marked on the side: "© DEE DEE DESIGNS 1964." Very hard to find. *Value:* $45.

CASES

WISHNIK®: These are two *Wishnik* carrying cases made by the Ideal Toy Corporation. The one on the left is much harder to find. It has the same look on the outside as the other house but inside it features a 3-D molded plastic cave scene with a waterfall. One side is for "Niks." The other case has a plain background with two openings on the inside. One is marked "Niks" and the other is "Naks." *Value:* mint case with 3-D background, $35; plain background: $15-$20.

(Above)

BUNALLAN: Shown are the back and the front of a Bunallan *Troll Traveling Bag*. It is made out of vinyl. It comes with a cardboard box to hold clothes and accessories and a strap on the inside to hold a troll. The bag has snaps along the sides and is marked "Bunallan Inc. Japan" on the bottom. I have also seen this house in yellow. Hard to find. *Value:* $35.

(Right)

BUNALLAN: This is a felt troll bag. It is possibly a *Troll Nap-Sak* made by House of Ideas or it may be made by Bunallan. It has a zipper in the back and elastic at the top. This troll bag provides plenty of room to carry a 3in (8cm) troll and all her clothes. The handle has arms sewn onto it. This bag also came in blue felt. Very rare. The bag is unmarked. *Value:* $35.

TROLL FURNI-TURE: House of Ideas also produced a troll house and furniture. The house is a molded plastic cave. I have not yet found one. Shown are two rooms of furniture for the cave. On the left is a bedroom set and on the right is a patio set. These are very hard to find. *Value:* mint in package, $45 each; loose, $20; cave $50-$75.

CHAPTER XI
Troll Memorabilia

The photographs in this chapter depict most of the memorabilia made using trolls. This includes troll charms, jewelry, paper dolls, spoons, and even a cookie cutter. Despite the variety of troll merchandise pictured, there may be items not shown here. It is impossible to know about all of the troll merchandise made. Much of it is unmarked, and to this day I still find things I have not seen before. I am, for example, still looking for the troll coloring book and Halloween costume. I hope you enjoy the memorabilia in this chapter as much as I enjoyed discovering and writing about it.

MISCELLANEOUS

UNMARKED TROLL LAMPS: These two troll lamps feature 5½in (14cm) *Wishnik®* trolls glued to wooden bases. I bought these lamps four years apart and at two different places. When I purchased the first lamp, I was skeptical about its originality. When I found the second lamp four years later with the same troll, the same wooden base and the same shade, I knew both lamps were original. They are unmarked and are very rare. *Value:* each with shade, $75.

MARX: This is the *Troll Village* play set made by Louis Marx. I have taken out a few pieces to show what they look like. This play set comes with a scenic playmat. (Mine is missing.) Notice the small animal trolls. They are made out of hard plastic and are about 1 in (3cm) tall. Box is marked: "Miniature Play Set Troll Village by Marx. Hand painted by Artists. Louis Marx Company 1965, Made in Hong Kong." *Value:* complete, $85; missing mat, $50.

MARX: This is a small play set also manufactured by Marx. It is called *Troll Party*. It features trolls glued down onto a scenic playground. Box is marked: "Miniature Play Set Troll Party. Handpainted by Artists. By Marx Made in British Crown Colony of Hong Kong. © Louis Marx & Company Incorporated." Very rare. *Value:* mint in box, $50.

THINGMAKER: This is Mattel's "Thingmaker" which creates *Creeple Peeple*. It was made in 1965. Although the *Creeple Peeple* are not referred to as trolls on this box, they certainly appear to me to be trolls. One of the molds and the instruction booklet are shown beside the "Thingmaker" box. This box still has the mohair, clothes, molds, "Thingmaker," and the "goop" inside. Nicely illustrated box. *Value:* complete, $50.

HALLOWEEN COSTUME: Shown both in its package and unpacked is the Ben Cooper *Wishnik®* Troll Halloween costume. The costume itself is one-piece with a flannel front and satin arms and legs. Comes with plastic molded mask with red flocked hair. The costume is marked: "© 1965 D.T.E. Uneeda." Box is marked: "Ben Cooper Brooklyn N.Y. Wishnik © 1965 D.T.E. Uneeda." Very rare. *Value:* mint in box, $125; costume only, $50-$75. *Courtesy of Richard O'Krogly Collection.*

HALLOWEEN MASKS: Shown are three different Halloween masks. The one on the left is marked "Topstone" under the chin. This mask has orange fun fur hair stapled to the top. Painted facial features. Molded plastic. Eyes, nostrils, and mouth are cut out. Rare. *Value:* $40. The mask in the center is marked: "Made in France for Van Dam" on a sticker inside. His hair is stapled on. Painted facial features. Eyes, nostrils, and mouth are cut out. Very rare. *Value:* $50. The mask on the right is the *Wishnik®* face mask. These could be bought separately. The original price of 29 cents is marked on the back. Red flocked hair. Eyes and mouth cut out. *Value:* $35.

BIKE GRIPS: These bicycle hand grips were sold by Sears. They are molded red glitter rubbery grips. The trolls are in a seated position with their arms outstretched. Package marked: "Glitter Grips Lucky Troll, Royalty Design of Florida, Incorporated 1967 Pat. No. #3251241." Extremely rare. *Value:* mint in package, $100; pair, loose, $50-$65.

TROLL CAR: Shown is the troll car by Irwin. It is a molded hard plastic log-shaped car. It has a gold foil "grill" on the front. This is the only marking on the car. Sticker marked: "Irwin Wishnik REG'D T.M. of Uneeda Doll Company Incorporated © 1965 by Uneeda Doll Company Incorporated." Usually found with the grill missing. Rare. *Value:* $50-$65.

WHAMMY WINK COMB AND PIN: Shown on the left are two troll combs made by Wonderworld, who also made a troll pin. The trolls have plastic heads with nylon hair. One eye is open and the other eye "winks." Original poly bag with header. Label marked: "Whammy Wink™ Troll. Good Luck Clips on to pockets, sweaters etc. Synthetic hair. Sterile-Clean Winks-Peeks-A lucky charm. Made in U.S.A. by Wonderworld NO#100." Hard to find. *Value:* comb, mint in package, $25; pin, mint in package, $20.

RUBBERY TROLLS: These trolls remind me of old novelty erasers. They are made out of rubber and come with glued on mohair. The large troll has fun fur hair. Mohair is missing from the blue troll in the center. The small trolls are called *Fings*. They are all unmarked. The large one has plastic eyes. The others are painted. They are hard to find. *Value: Fing*, mint in package, $25; loose, $10-$15; large orange hair troll, $15-$20.

TROLL NOTEBOOK: This is a troll vinyl-covered notebook. Features seven Thomas Dam trolls. Marked: "Copyright 1964 SD." Very rare. *Value:* $45.

RECORD ALBUM: This record album was put out by Little World Records. It features three *Wishnik*® trolls on the cover. Back of album shows three other troll albums that were available. This was made in 1965. Hard to find. *Value:* with record, $75; cover only, $25-$40.

PAPER DOLLS: These paper dolls were made by Whitman. Features four trolls, two boys and two girls, with 26 different outfits. Cover is marked: "*Reg. T.M. of Uneeda Doll Company, Incorporated. C MCMLXV by Uneeda Doll Company, Incorporated. A Whitman Book® Western Publishing Company, Incorporated. Racine Wisconsin Produced in the U.S.A." These are easy to find. *Value:* mint and uncut, $20-$25.

BOOK: *It's a Dam Dam World* book, by Hal Goodman and Larry Klein. Hard cover. Features Dam trolls with whimsical sayings. Marked: "Copyright 1965 by Dam Things Est. Vaduz Liechtenstein." Easy to find. *Value:* $15.

MAGNETIC TROLLS: These two items are made by Smethport Specialty Company in 1965. On the left is a magnetic doodle troll. The wand was used to make faces on the troll. The other troll is a paper doll printed on heavy paperboard with magnetic clothes that stick to the paper doll. *Please Note:* Both of these items have been re-issued. The reissues come in the same packaging. The only difference is that the new packages include a UPC symbol. Please be careful when purchasing these at doll shows, flea markets, or antique shops. Value given is for old original issues. *Value:* magnetic doodle, $25. *Courtesy of Richard O' Krogly Collection. Value:* paperdoll, mint in package, $25.

METAL TROLLS
AND
JEWELRY

METAL MOLD: 3½in (9cm) tall heavy metal troll mold. Has a hole on top of head with threads to screw into a machine. Unmarked. Very rare. *Value:* $100+. *Courtesy of Richard O' Krogly Collection.*

TROLL PIN: 1¼in (5cm) tall gold-tone metal troll pin. Has fun fur hair and jiggly eyes. Unmarked. *Value:* $10-$12.

CLIP-ON: Back view of 1¼in (5cm) tall gold metal (worn) troll clip-on. Looks like pin on the left. Purple fun fur hair with jiggly eyes. Shown on his back so you can see the clip. Unmarked. Harder to find than pins. *Value:* $25.

METAL TROLL PIN: This 1in (3cm) metal troll head is a pin. It is marked: "REG. DES. 904-395" on back. Very rare. *Value:* $35-$40. *Courtesy of Lisa Kerner Collection.*

KOREAN PIN: 1½in (4cm) tall gold-tone metal troll pin. Has white mohair and painted facial features. Marked: "Made in Korea" on back. Hard to find. *Value:* $25.

SILVER PIN: 1in (3cm) tall hard plastic silver colored pin. Large rhinestone eyes. Red painted mouth. Marked: "Hong Kong" on the pinback. Hard to find. *Value:* $15.

STERLING CHARM: 1in (3cm) tall sterling silver Norwegian looking troll charm. Marked: "NORGE." *Value:* $10-$12.

PEWTER PENDANT: 1¾in (5cm) pewter pendant, which can also be worn as a pin. Marked: "Pewter H.S. Made in Norway" on back. *Value:* $18-$25.

UNMARKED NECKLACE: 1¾in (5cm) tall gold-tone metal troll necklace. Has jiggly eyes. Unmarked. *Value:* $25.

NECKLACE: 1½in (4cm) tall gold-tone metal troll necklace. Troll has five fingers per hand. Marked: "S.H.E. 1964" on back. Very rare. *Value:* $35.

PEWTER NECKLACE: 1in (3cm) tall pewter troll necklace. Marked: "Sweden BT" on back. *Value:* $15.

NECKLACE: ½in (1cm) hard plastic troll charm in clear plastic box. This is the smallest troll I have ever seen. Very hard to find. *Value:* $20.

UNMARKED: 1¼in (5cm) gold-tone metal troll welded onto a rocker. He has jiggly eyes and fun fur hair. Unmarked. Hard to find. *Value:* $25.
RING: ¾in (2cm) tall plastic troll head. Has rhinestone eyes and yellow nylon hair. He is a ring. Hard to find. *Value:* $20.
RING: 1in (3cm) tall brown plastic troll ring. The ring is also plastic. The troll can be taken off the ring. Hard to find. *Value:* $15.

CHARMS

ACME TOY CO.: Three 1in (3cm) charms with nylon hair on original blister card. Card marked: "© 1964 Acme Toy Corp. Chicago, 50 Ill. No. #350." *Value:* mint on card, $20.
HONG KONG: Three 1in (3cm) hard plastic charms with yarn hair. Black painted eyes. Original poly bag with header card. Marked: "Hong Kong." *Value:* $10-$12.
HONG KONG: These are the same trolls but with different packaging. *Value:* $10-$12.

118

MISCELLANEOUS CHARMS: One good way to display all of the many different troll charms you find is to purchase an inexpensive Lucite frame and sew the charms onto the frame's cardboard backing. I do not recommend gluing the charms on. The charms seen here range from 1in (3cm) to 2in (5cm) tall. The larger ones are pencil toppers and can still be found. They also come in a 1½in (4cm) size. They are marked "Hong Kong." The older charms are 1in (3cm) tall. Some come with yarn hair, nylon, or no hair. Some have painted eyes, and others have rhinestone eyes. Some have hats molded on; others have hats glued on. A wide

variety of charms can be found. Millions of these charms were made. The following prices provide a basic guide to values. *Value:* old 1in (3cm) charms with nylon hair, up to $3; with rhinestone eyes, up to $3; old hard plastic with yarn hair 1in (3cm) tall, up to $2; color 1in (3cm) old trolls, up to $4.

MISCELLANEOUS TROLLS

SKREWY SKWERT: Troll is 3in (8cm) tall. Green plastic body. Comes with white tubing with a bulb on the end. Fill with water, squeeze the bulb, water and comes out of the belly button. Original poly bag with header card. Marked: "It's a Finky Skrewy Skwert. Palmer Plastics Inc. Brooklyn 36 N.Y." The back of

the card has instructions. Hard to find. *Value:* mint in package, $45; loose, $25. *Courtesy of Richard O'Krogly Collection.*

BUBBLE GUM CARD: This is a display card for a bubble gum machine. 1in (3cm) hard plastic troll charms with yarn hair and painted eyes. Maker unknown. *Value:* $15.

KNICKERBOCKER: The two puppets on the left are made by Knickerbocker. One is a marionette and the other is a hand puppet. The marionette has a stuffed body and vinyl head. Painted facial features. Peach colored synthetic hair. Head is marked: "Knickerbocker 19©64 Japan." Also has sewn in label. He is called *Terry Troll* according to his label. He is 11in (28cm) tall.

Hand puppet is 9in (23cm) tall. It is also marked. *Value:* marionette mint in box, $85; loose, $60; handpuppet, $35.

GERMAN: This puppet is 12in (31cm) tall with long black mohair. Painted facial features. Papier-mâché type head. Cloth body. Label on clothing marked: "ERI SPIEL MADE IN GERMANY." *Value:* $25.

SEXTON: This is a set of metal wall plaques. They are painted and range in size from 5in (13cm) to 3½in (9cm). They are a troll family and were also made as a one-piece coat rack. Hard to find. *Value:* complete set of wall plaques, $75-$85; coat rack, $100.

(Left to right)
JAPAN BANK: 6in (15cm) tall ceramic bank. White floss-like hair. Brown plastic eyes. Jumper painted on. Base marked: "Lucky Bank." Marked: "Made in Japan" on bottom. Hard to find. *Value:* $40.

WHISKEY JUG: 10in (25cm) tall. Brown glazed ceramic whiskey jug with ceramic troll on top. He has long white mohair glued onto his head. Unmarked. Very rare. *Value:* $75-$85.

TROLL *SALT AND PEPPER:* These troll salt and pepper shakers are 3in (8cm) tall. They have rabbit fur hair pasted on top of their heads. Holes are in back. Clothes are painted on. Do not use a harsh cleaner or scrubbing pad on them because the paint comes off easily. A sticker on the bottom is marked "Reg. U.S. Pat. Off. Norcrest Japan." Hard to find. *Value:* set, $45.

(Above left)
COOKIE CUTTER: Cookie cutter is aluminum and 3½in (9cm) tall. This was a mail-in offer. I have part of the original magazine advertisement, which includes a picture of Wrigley's spearmint gum. Wrigley's was apparently the company offering the cookie cutter set. The set came with a frosting tube and tips. Recipes and instructions also were included. It is very rare to find the set complete in its original mailing box as shown here. *Value:* as shown, $75; cookie cutter only, $25.

(Above right)
SPOONS: Here are two souvenir silver plated teaspoons. The one on the left is marked "Sunndal Sora 60 Grms" on the back of the handle. The other is marked "NORGE" on the bowl, and its box is marked "K-Produkter-NORGE." These can be found in Scandinavian shops. *Value:* $6-$10 each.

WISHNIK® PURSE: Clear plastic coin purse. Features a *Wishnik* bride and a girl troll. These came out in 1983. Marked: "C Uneeda Doll Company, Licensed by Uneeda Doll Company Incorporated, 1983 Laramie." *Value:* mint on card, $15.

PUFFY STICKERS: These puffy stickers were also issued in 1983. They have a Canadian label. *Value:* mint in package, $6-$8.

IRWIN TROLL: 14in (36cm) tall. Covered in purple fun fur. Stuffed body with large plastic eyes. Yarn mouth. He is *Irwin Troll* from the *Broom Hilda* cartoon. Original paper tag. Marked: "Wallace Berrie & Sons 1980." *Value:* mint with tag, $25. Next to *Irwin* is *Irwin Troll* bubble bath. Hat is missing. Made in 1977. *Value:* as shown, $10; with hat, $15. On the right is troll soap. Box is marked: "Dr. Zud's Terrible Troll!" On the back of the soap is marked: "© 1979 Hallmark Cards." *Value:* mint in box, $15.

CHAPTER XII
Newer Trolls

The trolls in this chapter were issued in recent years. You will be able to find some of these trolls at stores now. In the 1990s as I write this book, another troll craze is going on. I am presenting a few of the many, many troll items out on the market. It is impossible to show all of the companies that are marketing trolls today because more and more troll merchandise is coming out weekly! I have not listed values for troll items that were available at the time this book was written. Troll items manufactured in recent years but no longer available do have val-

GERMANY: The trolls pictured came out three years ago. They were made in Germany. The boy and girl on the left are 6in (15cm) tall. They have white fun fur hair, black plastic eyes, and original clothes. They are unmarked. Original cellophane bag with header card. Card is marked: "MADE IN GDR Art 09024." The 3in (8cm) boy and girl are shown on the right. *Value:* 6in (15cm) size, mint in box, $12; 3in (8cm) size, $4.50.

HOBNOBBINS™: *Hobnobbins* came out in 1989. They were created by "Those Characters From Cleveland, Inc." and distributed by Playschool, Inc. Twenty-four different styles of these stuffed trolls were made. I have also seen lunchboxes with thermoses, slippers, slipper socks, shampoo, and bubble bath sets from *Hobnobbins*. You may still find these in toy stores. Shown are the *Grandpa* and *Grandma Hobnobbins*. *Value:* stuffed trolls, mint in box, $10.

GAMES WORKSHOP: The items pictured are made by Games Workshop Product, a company based in England. Games Workshop has a store in Maryland. They make fantasy role-playing lead figures for games playing. Pictured are lead trolls from various games that can be painted. From the left are trolls from the *Marauder* series, 1988, the *Blood Bowl* series, and the *Citadel* series. Four different troll games were also made. Shown are *Trolls in the Pantry* and *Squelch!* Not shown are *Hungry Troll* and *Oi! Dats My Leg!* These were made in 1989. All came with a cassette tape of troll silly songs. If you would like more information, you can write to: Games Workshop, Inc., 3431 Benson Avenue, Baltimore, MD 21227.

MISCELLANEOUS TROLLS: Shown on the left is the troll character from the movie *Willow*. These were made by Tonka Toys. *Value:* mint on card, $3. Next are two heart-shaped boxes of Valentine's Day candy. Each has a 1½in (4cm) plastic-pencil topper troll wrapped in cellophane on top. You may still find these around the holiday. Candy is made by Warners in Chicago. *Value:* $1.50. Next are troll barrettes by Rosecraft Kids. Hard plastic one-piece molded trolls. Unmarked. *Value:* $6. On the right is the troll from the *Gnomes* series. It comes with a story about the *Gnomes*. The troll is a 2¼in (7cm) PVC figure marked: "© 1980 UNIEBOEK B.V." and "Made in Hong Kong" on bottom of feet. *Value:* mint in package, $4.50.

NORFINS®: These Norfin® *Jester Trolls* are no longer available. They are 6in (15cm) tall with various colors of synthetic hair. Dark brown plastic eyes. One-piece stretchy knit outfit. Marked: "DAM © 1988, Made In Denmark" on bottom. *Value:* $25.

NORFINS: Shown are two of the many styles of Norfin® trolls made by EFS Marketing Associates Inc. They make a wide variety of trolls ranging in size from 1½in (4cm) to 18in (46cm) tall. These are the *Little Tykes* style. EFS has been making trolls for many years.

WISHNIK®: Shown here are the newest *Wishnik* trolls made by Uneeda Doll Company. They have re-issued their 8in (20cm), 5½in (14cm) and 3in (8cm) sizes. The 3in (8cm) size comes nude. The other two sizes are dressed in various costumes. All have double horseshoes on the bottoms of their feet. They have synthetic hair and are made of vinyl.

RUSS® TROLLS: Shown here are two of the many different styles of trolls made by Russ Berrie. Russ trolls range from 1in (3cm) to 20in (51cm) in size. Trolls are vinyl with synthetic hair and plastic eyes. These are examples of the 5in (13cm) size.

TREASURE TROLLS™: These trolls are made by Ace Novelty Company. Their trolls have "Wishstones®" in their belly buttons. The trolls are vinyl with synthetic hair and colored plastic eyes. Ace makes trolls ranging in size from 3in (8cm) to 20in (51cm). Shown also is a *Treasure Troll* watch.

APPLAUSE: Here are two of the twelve different styles of *Magic Trolls*™ made by Applause Toys. These are troll babies. They have jointed arms and legs, and their heads turn. Applause also makes a larger stuffed troll.

LARGO TROLLS: Shown are three trolls manufactured by Largo Toys Ltd. They made three different *Santa Fe Trolls*, four different *California Trolls*, and three different *Rock N' Roll Trolls*. A picture of bride and groom trolls is on the back of these packages. I believe the bride and groom were never put on the market because no one I know has been able to find them. Largo no longer sells trolls. Now Toys N Things markets these trolls. The same troll mold is used; only the packaging is different. *Value:* Largo Trolls only, mint on card, $4.50.

TOYS N THINGS: Here are some of the different trolls and troll merchandise marketed by Toys N Things. From the left: a 5in (13cm) baby troll, an 8in (20cm) bank, and a hip-pack that holds three trolls.

127

ABOUT THE AUTHOR

Debra Clark has been collecting trolls for 12 years. She saved her original seven trolls from childhood. She has kept her favorite turtle troll on her dresser through the years. Her husband and she went to a flea market where she bought a 7in bank troll. That purchase triggered a quest to find more of her favorite childhood dolls. Now some 1800 trolls later, she still is out there searching for more trolls to add to her collection. "Trolls are fascinating, each one has a different look to them and they are hard to resist in the eye of the collector!" Debra is 33 and resides in Northern Illinois with her husband and two daughters.

Front cover:
Thomas Dam *Robin Hood.* 7½in (19cm) *Value:* $65-$75. (*See page 66.*)
Dam Things Est. Black Troll. 12in (31cm). *Value:* redressed, $200; original clothing, $300+. (*See page 20.*)
Dam Things Est. Turtle. 3¼in (8cm). *Value:* $150-$250. (*See page 11.*)

Title page:
Unmarked boy, 7¾in (20cm) and unmarked girl, 7in (18cm). *Value:* pair, $125; each, $60. (*See page 37.*)
Back cover:
Thomas Dam boy. 8½in (22cm). *Value:* with girl (*see page 37*), $150; dressed, $75; nude, $50. *Courtesy of Richard O'Krogly Collection.*